EGYPT'S QUEEN
Cleopatra

Down through the centuries, the story of Cleopatra has gripped the imagination. No fiction could rival the drama that was her life. Queen of Egypt at the age of seventeen, loved by Julius Caesar and Marc Anthony, hers was a life of triumph and tragedy in which the political intrigues of the ancient world combined with an immortal love story to give us a portrait of a woman who had to struggle not only against her enemies but against her heart as well. Written with drama, yet faithful to recorded history, this is the moving and fascinating story of Egypt and Rome of 2,000 years ago and of one of the most romantic heroines of all time.

Books by Iris Noble

Biographies

CLARENCE DARROW

THE COURAGE OF DR. LISTER

THE DOCTOR WHO DARED
William Osler

GREAT LADY OF THE THEATRE
Sarah Bernhardt

JOSEPH PULITZER
Front Page Pioneer

NELLIE BLY
First Woman Reporter

WILLIAM SHAKESPEARE

FIRST WOMAN AMBULANCE SURGEON
Emily Barringer

EGYPT'S QUEEN
Cleopatra

PHYSICIAN TO THE CHILDREN
Dr. Béla Schick

NURSE AROUND THE WORLD
Alice Fitzgerald

EMPRESS OF ALL RUSSIA
Catherine the Great

Novels

ONE GOLDEN SUMMER

STRANGER NO MORE

THE TENDER PROMISE

MEGAN

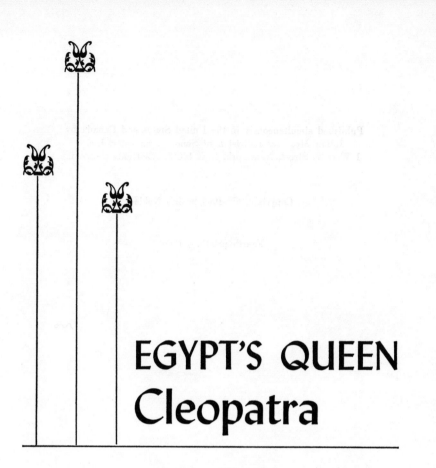

EGYPT'S QUEEN
Cleopatra

by Iris Noble

JULIAN MESSNER   New York

Printed in the United States of America

Library of Congress Catalog Card No. 63-8641

Author's Note

Source material for this book was found mainly in Plutarch's lives of Antony, Caesar and Octavian, through which he weaves his account of Cleopatra. Plutarch was partial to Greek heroes; fair to Romans; more prejudiced against such outsiders as the Egyptian queen, though she was Greek by birth. I studied numerous books in the British Museum in London and also in the San Francisco libraries, and found the scholarly account *Cleopatra— Her Life and Reign* by Désiré de Bernáth and the popular account of *Cleopatra* by Emil Ludwig to be most helpful. The books do not always agree on details of her life; they disagree most on the manner of her death. I have selected those accounts which seem most probable and accurate.

The character of Saat is purely fictional. I felt it necessary to embody in one man the comment, protest and ambition of the Egyptian people, since Cleopatra was removed from them by her position as queen and by her Greek heritage.

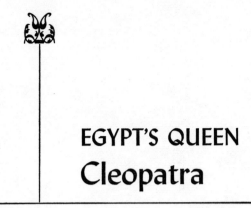

EGYPT'S QUEEN
Cleopatra

ONE

"Demetrius, what do these words mean—*filial love?*"

As she asked the question the girl looked up from the papyrus scroll she was studying. She leaned her elbows on the yellow and white alabaster table and cupped her chin in her hands. Hopefully, she scrutinized the face of her teacher.

Demetrius pulled at his white, curly beard before he answered. "Princess Cleopatra, surely that is a simple term to understand? *Filial* is the relationship of son or daughter to parent. *Love*—cannot you define love?"

She moved, impatiently. Her long, coppery-brown hair lay unbound around her shoulders. She tossed it back out of her eyes. "I know what filial means and I know the definition of love. My father is Auletes, Ptolemy the Eleventh. I am Cleopatra, his daughter. That is our relationship. But when poets and philosophers speak of filial love, filial duty, filial respect as being so very important I am not sure that I know their full meaning. They are just words to me."

"I cannot believe you speak seriously," Demetrius said. "I—"

Sosigenes, the astronomer, interrupted him. "How can she be expected to know? In this room I speak plainly." His voice was harsh. "Has she ever known the love of a parent?" He looked around at the other three teachers and then down at the slight figure of the thirteen-year-old girl. "Her mother is dead. Her father is a drunkard and a spendthrift and a fool, in debt to Romans who laugh at his antics, loan him money so that they can keep him prisoner in Rome until they decide what to do with us. How can the Princess be expected to feel love or respect or duty toward him?"

"Love and respect toward one's parents," objected the quiet Josephus, the Jewish teacher of languages, "is a natural impulse of the human being. A family is not a family without the emotions which bind parents and children together. Is there nothing in your heart, child, for your father, Auletes?"

"I feel sorry for him," she said, groping for the right way to express her vague emotions. "It is wrong for Berenice to try to take the throne away from him. She is wicked. My father is king, even if he is everything Sosigenes says of him. I will do whatever I can to help him. Is that loving him?"

She looked at the four of them in turn. Sosigenes had said that in this room he spoke plainly. It was so. When she had first come to the great museum to study she had been eleven and undisciplined. No slave or servant or attendant had ever argued with her or told her unpleasant truths. She had been startled that these scholars sought for reality, no matter how distasteful. She was furious when they said her reasoning might be wrong or faulty.

She made scenes. She called them names. She cried, stormed, ordered them to admit that a royal princess could not be wrong. They had been firm. Josephus had spoken for all of them when he told her, gently: "We risk our lives in letting you come here. Do not ask us to risk what is more precious to us than our lives: honor, truth, integrity."

That had been two years ago. She was glad they had fought her. She had learned to face facts; own up to her errors; and value this hard, constant search for exactness in what was known and for logical theories of what was not known.

The room had become for her and for them a place where they might speak freely. It was a small room, beautiful with its white stone pillars, its lofty ceiling and the open window which looked out to the harbor of Alexandria. It was a hidden room. Few people found their way there. Students and teachers and research scholars were familiar with the other, larger rooms in this vast building, but this one was known to only a few.

The Museum and Library of Alexandria was famous. Around it a great university had sprung up. The most renowned teachers came here. Among them, these four—Demetrius, Josephus, Sosigenes and old Serapion—were Cleopatra's friends.

Surely these men could help her solve the riddle of her strange life? "I think I feel pity," she continued her thoughts, "but not love. I do not think I have ever felt love. What is it?"

Sosigenes exploded, "Josephus, you say it is a natural impulse to love. How can a natural impulse grow in an unnatural family? The Ptolemies are cursed. Father has slain daughter, brother poisoned sister, wife killed husband, mothers destroyed their own children, for more than a hundred years. That is their history. You know it as well as I. This Greek family of the Ptolemy, who have ruled Egypt for centuries, have had no concept of love. They hate. They lust. They scheme. They kill. They do not love."

"Does that mean a Ptolemy cannot?" Josephus' hand fell kindly on Cleopatra's shoulder. "This one has intelligence."

Demetrius grumbled. "So did her early ancestors—"

"Yes." Cleopatra was on her feet with swift grace. She was a small girl, too thin for beauty. Only her eyes could be called attractive. They were large, with arched eyebrows, and they flashed with mental aliveness. "Demetrius is right. How can you say we are cursed? Alexander the Great gave Egypt to the first Ptolemy because that one was such a great Greek general. He helped conquer this land. Other Ptolemies built this museum and library. Where is there any such like it in the world? What other library has over seven hundred thousand manuscripts? What of the Ptolemies who encouraged art and culture and science and invention?"

Sosigenes stood his ground. "I am speaking of what goes on inside the royal palace. I am warning you, Princess, so you will not be like the others. The spilling of blood is not unique to the Ptolemies. Other royal families have murdered when it suited them, but the Ptolemies have long ago forgotten what it is to love."

Tiny, elderly, wrinkled Serapion, the mathematician, had been quietly rocking in his corner, taking no part in the discussion. Now he spoke. "How can the child forget what she does not know? Josephus' wisdom and Sosigenes' shouting won't teach it to her. She pities her father. That is a good start. Nurture that feeling, Princess. But now get on with your studies and let an old man have peace to do his mathematical calculations."

For an hour she read Homer under Demetrius' guidance. Then she had a lesson in Syrian with Josephus. "Your Latin and Greek are excellent," he complimented her. "You need further work, however, in Syrian and Hebrew, Persian, the Ethiop and Arabic languages."

The room was quiet. Only the rustle of the papyrus pages, the scratch of stylus pens, the low murmur of the voices of Cleopatra and Josephus were heard.

Suddenly the door opened. Cleopatra looked up, startled. Where was the slave who was supposed to guard that door against intruders?

Two young men lounged in the open doorway, leisurely looking about them. "There is nothing here, Titus," one said. "It must be simply a retreat for these old scholars."

"You are right." They both spoke Greek but this one had the accent of a Roman. "There is nothing here. Besides, I am fatigued. We have been an entire day strolling through this

museum. Tomorrow I begin my studies. I swear by Venus that
I have been less tired in a chariot race in Rome than in visiting
all these halls and rooms, these libraries, these dining halls and
galleries. Who but these decadent Alexandrians would put so
much money into books and learning—wait! Did you say there
was nothing here? Do you see what I do? A young female in a
place of study; this is incredible."

The situation appealed to Cleopatra's sense of humor. She put
her hand on Josephus' arm as he started to rise and silence the
two insolent young men. It was she who rose and walked timidly
across the room to the door.

"My lords," she said, letting her hair hang down over her face
and lowering her eyes, demurely, "good masters, do not disturb
the wise scholars. You think it strange that I am here? Cannot
even old men have young slave girls to fetch and carry the papyrus scrolls for them?"

"Shocking," said the one called Titus. "I have heard stories
of the strange customs of these people, but for learned men to
coddle themselves with the services of a slave girl is worse than
I thought. Come away," he said.

When they were gone and Cleopatra closed the door, she leaned
her head on it and laughed.

"You have caused a scandal," reproved Demetrius.

"You should not have said that. It was a falsehood," said
Josephus.

"You behaved most unbecoming a modest girl and a princess,"
admonished Sosigenes.

Suddenly from old Serapion came a wheeze and a choke and a
gurgle and then a burst of snickers and titters. It was too much
for the other teachers, and they, too, began to laugh. Cleopatra
fell onto a bench and rocked her small body back and forth,
holding onto her sides. "It is so good," she gasped out, finally, "to
laugh. I so seldom have the chance. Forgive me."

Sosigenes wiped his eyes. "If the truth be admitted, Princess,

I think we old men welcome your presence here as much for such pranks as for our pride in having such a brilliant student." His face grew sober. "Come, back to your lessons. You have much to learn."

The two intruding students had reason to be surprised. Young girls, in the year 56 B.C., did not attend universities. Even a royal princess would study in her own rooms, under one or two tutors. It would be enough if Cleopatra knew how to read and write Latin and Greek.

Cleopatra, the second oldest child of Auletes, Ptolemy XI, had begun her scholastic life in no way different from her sisters and brothers. By the time she was nine her father had learned that this girl had an unusually quick mind. She had learned everything her tutors could teach her; she demanded more. This tickled Auletes' vanity. In one of his few sober moments he took her to the museum to show her to the scholars and brag about his precocious child.

She was not to become a student there. No, a princess must abide by court rules. She fretted and stormed; threw papyrus scrolls at her next tutor; resigned herself to learning how to go through court etiquette, how to speak to this one and that as was thought necessary for a princess.

The unusual mind of this unusual girl might have become permanently stunted, but for an event which changed her life.

Ptolemy XI was rich, but his insatiable appetite for pleasure brought him into debt to powerful Romans. The country of Rome was more powerful than the country of Egypt; his debtors commanded that he pay them a visit and bring their money. He had gone but they would not settle. He and his debts had become a weapon in the hands of Rome. They kept him there, dangling on a puppet string, while they made up their minds what to do with him and Egypt. Should they let him remain king or should they sweep this fabulously wealthy country of the Egyptians into their own lap, as a province of Rome?

One of the leaders of Rome, a man named Caesar, took advantage of the situation. He took the island of Cyprus and deposed the man who was ruling it, the brother of Auletes.

This was too much for the Egyptians. Cyprus was theirs. They were not strong enough to turn their anger against Rome. They made Auletes, Ptolemy XI, their scapegoat; deposed him in his absence and put his oldest daughter, Berenice, on the throne.

This they had done in 58 B.C. When Berenice put on the crown, Cleopatra was in mortal danger. Berenice was her half-sister, the daughter of the King's first wife. She was ugly in face, form and heart. She feared all of her half-sisters and brothers, young as they were, because they were potential threats to her. She was a stupid woman so she particularly hated the intelligent Cleopatra.

She would have had the girl killed without a qualm except that the Alexandrian nobles who backed her forbade it—yet. They had put Berenice on the throne, but they needed official recognition of her sovereignty from Rome, otherwise the crown wobbled. It might not look well to start her reign with the murder of her sister.

Cleopatra knew the tightrope she walked. Any minute word might come that Rome had decided in favor of Berenice and not in favor of Auletes. Any moment Berenice's savage nature might break bounds. She had been known to kill a slave for accidentally stepping on the hem of her robe.

Olympus, physician to the palace, warned the girl, "Keep out of her sight, Princess Cleopatra. Hide. If she does not see you often, she will not think so much about you."

Hide, yes—but where? The palace was enormous. Its gardens and rooms and banquet halls and galleries, throne room, audience chambers, servants' quarters, slave cells, kitchens and service rooms stretched the full length of the Lochias Promontory, enclosed by a high wall. This promontory was like a wide finger reaching out to the Mediterranean Sea from the city of Alexandria. On both sides of it were harbors. At its sea end was the Pharos Lighthouse.

Vast as it was it was ridden with spies and gossips and torn by factions. Cleopatra's slightest move would be reported.

In this emergency she remembered the library. It fronted on the harbor only a short distance from the palace. She could spend her days there. Only at night then, in her apartments, would she be in peril.

The library became a refuge. Her four teachers risked danger because they were proud of her brilliance. With them she studied astronomy, history, mathematics, physics, rhetoric, literature, philosophy, poetry, drama and languages.

The shadows in the small, secret room grew long. Cleopatra rolled up the scroll she was studying and sighed. It was time to return to the palace.

Her slave awaited her outside the door. "You left your post this afternoon," she said, angrily.

"Forgive me, Princess," he begged. "I thought I had a chance to learn some news for you. You ordered me to listen when I heard anything of Rome."

"What did you hear?" She followed him to a private side door.

"I could not understand it. They were new students from Rome, and they talked a lot about a man named Caesar. I did not understand. I thought it was a man called Pompey who was king—"

"You are stupid," she said. "They do not have kings. They elect consuls. Pompey has been the great one as long as I remember. I don't know this Caesar, except that he was the general who stole Cyprus. I hope Pompey kills him."

"The students said Pompey and Caeser were friends—" the slave began to speak but she hushed him. They were outside. She drew a cloak around her which concealed all of her, including her head. She stepped into a litter, which was hoisted to the shoulders of four slaves. Through a curtain in it she could see out but not be seen.

They went past the museum and library, the theatre and the Temple of Pan. Across the street, between warehouses, she caught glimpses of the harbor. There were dozens of ships in it—galleys, trading vessels, triremes, small pleasure boats. Goods were being ferried to and from the docks.

She was carried past piled sacks of rice and grain from the Nile Valley. Her litter dodged the long human chain of workmen and slaves who lined the quay, passing boxes and sacks from one to another. She could smell pitch and tar from the boats; wine in casks; spices from the East; the rich fragrance of fruit.

Along the harbor sauntered the merchants and traders. Beggars followed them, whining for coins, ready to run at the approach of a harbor guard.

A chariot rattled over the stones. "Give way!" cried the charioteer. Cleopatra's slaves moved hastily to one side to avoid being hit by the two charging horses. She saw Achillas, the best Egyptian general, standing upright in the chariot. He was an arrogant man, this Achillas, she thought. He would bear watching.

Then she was through the gates of the palace. Just inside was a long, palm-shaded pavilion. It was a favorite with the aristocrats of Alexandria who came there to exchange gossip. The litter which bore Cleopatra went slowly here. Her slaves had orders not to push their way through or call attention to themselves. Also, going slowly she could look and listen. Sometimes she heard things she could convey by secret messenger to her father.

Two wealthy matrons were talking about fashion when they were joined by a man. He was Pothinus. Cleopatra's brother Ptolemy was in his charge, but he had made himself more important than that position warranted. Though he had neither rank nor wealth he was recognized as a force in the palace. He had his ways of knowing things before others did.

Cleopatra shifted her body to the right. Her slaves knew her silent commands and they also went to the right, close to the group where Pothinus was. She wanted to hear better. It was difficult because Pothinus was whispering. She could only hear: ". . . at last . . . Berenice sent . . . it is true . . . envoys to Rome with . . . don't ask me how much . . . a fortune, perhaps. . . ."

She had heard enough. With shaking hands she rapped three times. Her slaves went faster, hurrying around people, rushing along the pavilion paths.

It wasn't fast enough for her. She murmured, even though they couldn't hear her, "Hurry! Run—I may be too late!"

The whispered words had been clear to her. Berenice had at last sent her official envoys to Rome to insist upon her recognition as queen. They would go with an enormous fortune to bribe the Romans. Cleopatra must get word to her father at once.

As soon as she was in her own apartments she commanded Charmian, her attendant: "Go to the outer pavilion. Bring Appolodorus to me instantly, but let no one see you do it."

She could trust Appolodorus. He had acted as go-between before, bringing her messages that sea captains had slipped to him, from her father in Rome. While she waited for him she wrote the letter and sealed it and had it ready when the young man entered.

"Do you know of a captain willing to take chances?" she asked, handing him the letter. "One who will get the utmost speed from his ship and race those envoys to Rome? The envoys must have left last night or this morning."

"This morning; Pothinus said so." Appolodorus' handsome face looked as carefree and thoughtless as that of any other young Alexandrian of the fashionable class, but he had a rare and steadfast loyalty to both the King and this daughter. "There is one captain who might be persuaded to sail tonight and work his galley slaves hard, if he is paid well. He will want payment in advance—a lot of it."

Cleopatra left him for a second and came back with her jewel case. Diamonds and rubies which had once been her mother's she now gave to him. "Bargain with him as best you can but let not a single jewel stand in the way of success."

Appolodorus bowed and left.

Weeks of anxiety and tension went by. The whole palace felt it. By turns, Berenice seemed to be riding the crest of confidence that she would be queen, or screaming at her attendants and advisers when her nerves became fearful. More than ever Cleopatra tried to stay away from her. She came back from the library much later than before and stayed hidden in her own rooms and gardens.

One evening, late, she and Charmian and Iras were in her small garden by the lotus pool. Palm trees were graceful shapes in the twilight. The air was still warm.

Both Charmian and Iras were maidens of noble family. They were in waiting on the Princess, but because all three were so much the same age they were more friends than attendants. Charmian pulled a lotus flower out of the pool and held it in her cupped hands. Iras had placed a lump of scented oil on the top of her curls, in the Egyptian custom, and was enjoying the sweetness and coolness of it as it melted and ran down her cheeks.

Cleopatra sat on a bench a little distant from them. Behind her was a thick fig tree, and all around her hung grapes from a trellis. Back of the fig tree was a low wall supporting open stone grillwork.

The two girls were playing their favorite game while she listened. It was called "if Cleopatra were queen—"

"If you were queen, Cleopatra, I think you should forbid anyone in the palace eating onions. Berenice must adore them. The smell comes up from the kitchens. It is horrible."

"If you were queen, Cleopatra, you could pass for the goddess Isis. Your features are Grecian but you are shaped like an Egyptian. You are slim."

"Shall I show you how Berenice looks?" Cleopatra darted a

quick glance about her then stood up and postured before the other girls. She was a superb mimic. Her shoulders slumped and seemed to grow thick; her legs waddled as though they held much weight. She scowled.

"So—!" The child who had come stealthily into the garden surprised them all. "This is the way you mock our beloved older sister? What will you give me not to tell?" She had the face of a child but the eyes of a strange and cruel animal.

"I give you nothing, Arsinoë. You are not wanted here. Go back to your own rooms." Cleopatra held her voice steady but her heart was pounding. There was something wrong, something unhealthy about Arsinoë. She might tell Berenice, just for spite. Or she might not tell, for her own sly reasons which no one could guess.

"I shall go where I please and do as I please. I am not the danger to Berenice that you are. I am only ten and you are now fourteen. Even if they decide she is to be queen, she won't like you. Ganymede says that someday you might be a challenge to Berenice." Ganymede was her tutor. He was as mean and spiteful as Arsinoë. Cleopatra disliked them both.

Sosigenes was right, she thought sorrowfully. There is some taint or curse on our family. Arsinoë is cruel; one brother selfish and spoiled and the other a dull, sickly baby.

"Go away," she said, in quick anger, to Arsinoë. "You would be welcome to stay if you behaved nicely but I don't trust you."

She sat down on the bench and heard a faint rustle behind her. She froze like a statue, averting her head so that Arsinoë would not see her expression. The faintest of whispers reached her: "Princess—"

Without moving her lips she whispered back: "Wait. Say nothing." She watched Arsinoë dawdling by the pool; saw her rip up water lilies wantonly and tear them to pieces while she laughed at Charmian's protest. Would her sister never go? Cleopatra was in agony. She knew who the whisperer was and what it meant.

At last Arsinoë threw the lilies, with their muddy roots, into Charmian's face and ran off. While Iras was helping Charmian clean the dirt off, Cleopatra whispered, "Now—speak. It is safe. But softly so the maids do not hear." She trusted them, but if Berenice suspected anything she could torture information from them.

"Princess," came the whisper, "your father received the information you sent. Do you hear? He received it in time. He acted promptly. The envoys were seized when they landed and were killed before they could speak for Berenice. Your father took the money they had. He paid some of his debts."

"Yes. Go on. Quickly," she urged.

"The King made bold to press his claims to the Roman Senate. The wheel of fortune turned. Julius Caesar stood up and declared Auletes was the rightful king and that Egypt is an ally of Rome. I was told to repeat that: an ally of Rome."

The whisper stopped and she pleaded, "Is there no more?"

"Nothing, Princess. I must go." There was the tiniest rustle of leaves behind her, then there was silence. She got up, slowly. The rustle began again and she sank back on the bench.

"Forgive me," came the whisper again. "I am stupid. I forget the most important news. The Roman proconsul of Syria, one Gabinius, is desperate for our Egyptian gold to pay his soldiers there. Your father has offered him six thousand talents of gold from the royal treasury if Gabinius will march here with his legions and put Auletes back on the throne."

"Has Gabinius agreed?" she asked.

"I do not know," he said.

Though she waited a while, this time the whispering messenger had come to the end of his information. There was no further sound behind her.

Dangerous as it was both for him and for her, she must see

Appolodorus. She met him in her study room in the museum. The old scholars were discreetly absent. She told the young man the news.

"Does this mean that my father is once more rightful king and that Berenice is declared a usurper?" she asked him.

Appolodorus was even more excited than she. "It means more than that. I have been hearing more rumors about this Caesar. He and Pompey and a rich man, Crassus, have been named as a triumvirate to control all Rome and its colonies. Their term is limited by the Senate, but in fact they rule. They are supposed to be good friends but there is suspicion among the three. Caesar's territories, in the division among the three, are in the west— Gaul, Spain, Germany and Britain. I think he fears that Pompey will add Egypt to his possessions. By naming Egypt an 'ally' Caesar makes us equal with Rome; we are not a province to be taken over by Pompey. It was clever. It limits Pompey to the lands he already has."

What Rome did or did not do was unimportant to Cleopatra. "Will my father come? Do you think this Gabinius will accept his offer?"

"I don't know but we must be ready. Berenice will be a mad dog when she hears this. Eat no food that a slave has not already tested for poison. I know a loyal army captain. He will loan me four or five fighting men. We will dress them as slaves, smuggle them into your rooms, and they will guard every entrance day and night."

"Will you warn Pothinus so he can guard my brother?" She was trying not to be afraid but she was shivering.

Appolodorus' eyebrows went up. "Pothinus? He undoubtedly knows more than we, Cleopatra."

For more than two weeks she was guarded. She never left her rooms. Iras reported that Berenice's supporters had stopped coming to the palace. Servants gossiped in corners. The kitchens were in turmoil. Twice there was no hot water for Cleopatra's baths. Even when she slept she was aware of the restless prowling of her guards, and once she heard a scuffle. "What is it?" She crept to the door.

"A visitor, Princess. The ruffian had a knife. I broke his arm. Go back to sleep, please. I taught him a lesson," said the gruff soldier.

With a Roman army clearing the way for him and with the Roman general Gabinius leading the campaign, Auletes, Ptolemy XI, came home to Alexandria in triumph. It was a short and easy victory. The half-hearted opposition was swept away.

When the best Egyptian general, Achillas, went over to the side of the king with his army, Berenice was caught in a trap. Achillas was in Alexandria and he knew just who had favored her cause. He crushed them and went out of the gates to join the on-marching Gabinius.

Inside the palace all was confusion. When the Roman trumpets could be heard outside the palace walls, Cleopatra refused to stay in her rooms any longer. With her guards as protection and with Charmian and Iras following, she walked out into the lofty white stone halls. Some seemed deserted but in one great audience chamber she found throngs of the wealthy Alexandrian aristocrats.

They were frightened. Hands clutched at her. "Remember, Princess Cleopatra, that we never liked Berenice. . . ."

"My husband was forced into her Council—he was forced. . . ."

"We were your friends. . . ."

"Don't let those Romans use their swords on us. They are beasts, we hear. . . ."

She was only fourteen. She was astounded at their behavior. Were they such cowards? Did they think she had the power to help them?

Pothinus was by her side. He was a huge, fat man, whose smile was as oily as the grease he used on his hair. "Princess Cleopatra, may I have a word with you?"

"Speak. You have permission." Even his manner had changed and he was obsequious to her. It puzzled Cleopatra.

"I have labored," his tone was humble but his eyes were not. They were bold. "I have labored day and night these past days to bring the banquet hall and the audience chamber into such suitable elegance as will welcome our great Ptolemy and his Roman friends. I would not have these Roman barbarians think we have some rude court. The kitchens were disorganized but I now have ready the finest wines, the meats, the fruits for the homecoming banquet. Magicians and musicians and dancing girls are hired for entertainment. The throne room is hung with new golden curtains."

Grudgingly, she had to say, "You have worked wonders, Pothinus."

"There is one thing more. All of Alexandria will be showering gifts on the King to show loyalty. Of course, Ptolemy has no reason to doubt his daughter, and I hope you will assure him he has had no reason to dislike me, Pothinus. But there is a gift I could give him—it will need your permission—" he hesitated.

"What is it?" she asked.

"The head of Berenice." He hurried to explain, as if he had to urge this thing, "She is hiding in her chambers. Her guards have deserted her. We run no danger from her. It would be easy."

"No! You would not kill her when she was a powerful danger to the King. Now when she is helpless—no, Pothinus, let my father do what he pleases." She turned away from the frustrated anger in his face. She knew he was furious because he had hoped to make himself a prominent favorite of the King's with this bloody act.

She was saved further argument from him by the rush of people to windows and doors. Drums, trumpets and pipes could be heard at the gates. The King and the Romans were here.

When Auletes, Ptolemy XI, mounted the steps of his palace the first person he saw waiting for him at the top was his daughter Cleopatra. Courtiers lined the enormous entrance hall but she alone stood in the center of it, waiting, thrilled and excited, ready to welcome him with love.

He embraced her, casually.

"Welcome, my Father," she said. She looked up at his face.

What she saw shocked her. Weak tears of joy ran down his bloated, red-veined cheeks. His arm around her shoulder had no tenderness. He was smiling but not for her. He was saying, "At last! If you only knew what I have suffered—but it is all over. I am home. Faugh! You cannot imagine what it is like to live in an army tent. I am filthy. I want a bath. Stewards, take these gallant Roman officers to their apartments, but first send my musicians in so they may play for me while I bathe."

She stood and watched as he and the big mailed and helmeted figures of the Romans went down the hall. Her head drooped. Filial love—how could she feel love for this father? During the past year her imagination had dignified his memory a little. Now she knew he was still Auletes—the nickname so mockingly given him—"the Fluteplayer."

TWO

THE CONTRAST between the weak Auletes and the strong Roman officers was marked. At the banquet that night Cleopatra sat by her father's side; outwardly a proud girl, inwardly ashamed and close to tears.

The King of Egypt was a silly, capering, absurd figure of a man, whose tears flowed easily, who laughed too much and too loud. His hands were soft and white. He was quickly bored with serious matters, and his attention was fixed on the musicians and the entertainers.

The Roman officers had shed their tunic uniforms and donned robes, but their bare arms were bronzed and hard. Muscles corded their necks. Their faces were lean, tough, healthy and tanned by outdoor living. They drank wine but they did not grow maudlin as Auletes did.

Dining couches had been brought for them. They preferred them to the Egyptian chairs. Yet, even reclining as they ate, they looked ready to spring at any emergency. Auletes, Cleopatra thought with bitterness, would have to be carried to bed.

Under the table her hands were tightly clasped. She was humiliated by her father. She deeply resented these Romans. What right did they have to look at each other and smile at her

26

father's capers? Why did they not act as guests? Logic told her
they were not guests. They were conquerors. They would let a
Ptolemy sit on his throne, as long as it suited their purpose.

She saw her father fix his eyes on the flute player. He beck-
oned. She put out her hand on his arm to restrain him. It would
be intolerable if he should indulge his passion for playing the
flute now, in front of these Romans.

Her touch made him look at her. "My little jewel," he said,
with drunken thickness, "my lotus blossom. Did I tell you, General Gabinius, that it was my daughter who warned me of what
Berenice was doing? She is a true Ptolemy, this one—this
Cleopatra . . ."

The captain of the horse, a handsome young Roman, smiled.
"The Princess must be a clever child, then; gifted with intelligence like yourself, King Auletes."

Cleopatra felt the sting of his sarcasm. Auletes thought he
meant the compliment.

"Nicely put, Marc Anthony. Yes, she is like me. Look upon
her, gentlemen, Roman lords, look at my daughter Cleopatra.
I call upon you to remember my wish and give her your support.
When the time comes for me to die," tears of self-pity overflowed
his eyes and he snuffled, "then she shall be queen of Egypt.
I order it so."

Pothinus had been hovering behind his chair. Now he stooped
and whispered.

"Hey? What?" Auletes stammered. "Yes, you are right,
Pothinus. I must add, my good Roman friends, that Cleopatra
will share her throne. It is our custom of many centuries that
sister and brother are married and become king and queen. A
Ptolemy must share the throne only with another Ptolemy."

Cleopatra saw the captain, Marc Anthony, turn aside and she
heard him say to a companion, "What a filthy custom, to marry
brother and sister!"

She was furious. Marriage between a royal sister and brother was part of Egyptian law and religion. True, it was frequently only a marriage in name. Auletes had taken two wives not related to him and not royal.

There was a mystery about Cleopatra's mother. Some said she was not even of Greek ancestry but of the tribe of Idumae or Edom, as it was called. It was rumored that Auletes had found her in that mountainous country near Judaea and fallen in love with her beauty. He had brought her back, passing her off as a Macedonian Greek. Cleopatra remembered her as a sad, beautiful, haunted, silent woman, cut off from her children by the etiquette of court life.

Cleopatra spoke and all those around her fell silent, startled by the presumption of a girl speaking before men and also by the clear, musical quality of her voice.

"The kings and queens of Egypt," she was remembering a lesson the temple priest had given her, "partake of the divine nature of our gods. Osiris was the god of the Nile. His sister, Isis, was the goddess all-feminine—sister, wife and mother. When Set killed Osiris, it was Isis and her sister Nephthys who found his body and concealed it. Isis raised her son, Horus, to manhood until Horus could revenge the death of his father, Osiris. Horus killed Set. By so doing he raised Osiris from the dead. The queen of Egypt is also Isis; the king is also Osiris. So they marry as the god and goddess did."

Captain Marc Anthony leaned across the table. His eyes were genuinely kind and full of admiration as he looked at her. "I apologize," he spoke softly so that no one else could hear, "for my rudeness. You are quite right, Princess Cleopatra, to defend so courageously your religion and your customs."

She smiled at him. He looked startled. He said, "Child, be careful of that smile. When you are older it will break hearts."

She could leave the banquet early because she was so young. In her own rooms she still heard faint sounds of the noisy revelry and music and laughter. The banquet would go on until dawn.

Even her warm, scented bath did not relax her. She was troubled. "I thought that when my father came home," she confided to Charmian as they prepared for bed, "there would be no more troubles."

"How can you be so gloomy tonight, Cleopatra? I thought you were celebrating? Iras and I envied you at the banquet. Tell me," coaxing, "about the magicians and the entertainers. And about the Romans. Are they monsters, truly?"

"They are men. Is Iras asleep? No, leave her sleep. I am unhappy. Let her sleep and dream about banquet food and handsome captains. These Romans are men, Charmian, but they are not like ours. It is a different breed. I heard them talking about us and they said Alexandrians are light-minded, witty and clever and fond of talk, but with no firmness of purpose."

"I don't like men who are too serious," Charmian pouted. "I want them to make me laugh."

Cleopatra was curled up on the top of her silk sheets on her bed. She leaned back against the cushions which lay on the carved ivory headrest. "Appolodorus is strong and he is clever. He acts quickly when he has to. Yet he hates to plan for a month ahead. He told me so. He wants to practice his lute and ride his chariot and meet his friends to gossip and talk."

"What troubles you, Cleopatra?" Charmian was sleepy and yawning from her couch.

"My father said tonight that I would be queen when he dies. I've thought about that before, but I never knew what it meant. How can I be a real queen when Rome is so strong and Rome decides what Egypt will do? Even that captain and that general in the banqueting room thought they were our masters. They only concealed it with politeness. These Romans could make us a province. They could divide us into pieces. I could be a queen without a country. What am I going to do, Charmian?"

From the other couch came only the slow, fluttering breath of a girl fast asleep.

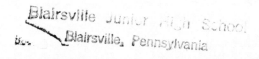

Cleopatra pulled the sheet over her, but she lay awake a while longer. It used to be just a name to me—*Rome*—she thought. The whole country of Italy was called "Rome" because its principal city dominated it as it dominated most of the known world. She would have to learn more about those strange people.

Pompey was the name she knew best—Pompey the Great, the general who was considered the best, until this Julius Caesar came along. Demetrius told her that Caesar had gone farther west and north than was believed possible and had conquered Gaul and then crossed over some water to a place named Britain.

Now Caesar was the hero. The third one of the triumvirate was important only because of his wealth.

In the days and months that passed, life in the palace reverted to the way it had been when Cleopatra was a child. The Roman officers left. Two of their legions remained to help Auletes in case of trouble, but there was no trouble. Auletes permitted his advisers to do as they pleased, so long as they did not interfere with his fun. The palace was once again full of his old roistering, drunken, pleasure-loving companions.

Berenice was executed. Even the memory of her faded fast. Arsinoë and the seven-year-old Ptolemy strutted around the palace, enjoying their freedom, accompanied always by their tutors, by their guardians and by fawning, flattering sycophants.

The youngest child of Auletes was still a baby. He was ignored by his father and the rest of his family; court etiquette separated them; even this baby had his own nurses and his own apartments. He lived contented and coddled.

Only Cleopatra was unhappy. She watched and observed. She could not forget how much more kingly the Romans had appeared than Auletes. She wondered who was actually running the affairs of Egypt. Since she could no longer go to the museum —Auletes had been shocked at her request—she found life dull and heavy.

Though Auletes usually ignored his children, he did notice her unhappy face. "Why do you not smile?" he demanded, fretfully. "Your manner annoys me. After all I have suffered, must I come back to your frowns and pouts? Your sister Arsinoë is amusing and gay. She pleases me more than you do."

The hint was very clear. It shocked Cleopatra into action. Auletes was shallow and so fickle that he might easily set her aside and name Arsinoë as his heir to the throne if Cleopatra offended him. She must do something to win back his favor.

She was not yet fifteen. She had no one to constantly urge her forward, as Theodotus and Pothinus did the young Ptolemy, or as Ganymede did for Arsinoë. This was her own fault. She had refused, when still a child, to be led around by such men nor could she be fooled by their flattery.

After a week of worrying, she made up her mind what she must do. Appolodorus and Olympus must help her. She summoned them, along with Iras and Charmian.

"It is time," she told them, "that I stop being the student and take my place in the society of the palace. I am ignorant of fashionable life. I plan to give a party and invite my father and all of Alexandria's aristocracy to it, so that they may begin to know me as their future queen."

Olympus, the physician, smiled at such pretentious words from such a young girl, but Appolodorus was more worldly. His eyes sparkled. He said, "Excellent! I can tell you that the Alexandrian nobles grumble. Auletes prefers his drunken rascals to them. They feel snubbed and shut out of the palace life. Would you hold the party here, Cleopatra? Then you must redecorate. These rooms have not been changed since your nursery days."

She looked about her and nodded. Iras and Charmian were excited. "You go to all the wealthy homes, Appolodorus," Charmian said. "You can advise us. Is there a particularly beautiful one we can copy?"

"No." Cleopatra was determined. "I will not follow fashion. I will set it. I must startle everyone, including Auletes. I cannot be just another rich girl. A princess is expected to be different. I overheard some ladies talking one day about fashions. They said it was now smart to adapt a little of the old Egyptian style to our Grecian art. So I shall decorate these rooms completely Egyptian, as in the days of the Pharaohs. I shall dress, for the time being, as the Egyptians dressed."

"No white robes? No chitons? Are you not going to do your hair up in the Grecian style?" Iras was astounded.

But now that she knew what she wanted, Cleopatra's mind worked like lightning. "Appolodorus, scour the city for craftsmen who still work in the old manner, or find modern ones who will imitate the art of the Third Dynasty. Iras, call the best tailors and seamstresses. Charmian, I wish to speak with the head gardener. I want the best goldsmiths and silverworkers and sculptors here, today."

Appolodorus was enthusiastic. "There is a new shipment of copper objects in the harbor today. The Thos family has offered a large sum for just one copper screen, inlaid with pearls and malachite."

"Outbid them, Appolodorus," Cleopatra ordered recklessly.

"The most clever seamstress is a a slave belonging to Rebecca, wife of Benjamin, the shipowner," said Charmian.

"Buy that slave at any price."

"But, child, where will you get the money for all this," Olympus objected. "Your father is too greedy to be lavish with you. His own expenditures are already causing murmurs throughout the city."

Cleopatra had already considered this. "Have you seen the petitioners crowding around the palace gate? Everyone wants something: a permit to unload at a better wharf; a pardon for a son taken in crime; a trading concession with our Nubian chiefs. Spread the word, Appolodorus, but quietly, that I have the ear of the King. They must apply to me. I will see they are heard

without delay. That is all I will promise them—that they be heard
—but they must pay me."

Olympus raised his eyebrows. "That is a common practice
but not by a girl of fourteen. You will antagonize some of the
King's councilors who consider these bribes as belonging to
them."

"I cannot help that." She was learning to be ruthless when it
was necessary. "I cannot please everyone. At the moment, it is
most important that I please my father."

"Then may I make a suggestion?" said Olympus. "Your
father's eye may be pleased at new decorations, but he is more
interested in music. You cannot, in modesty, provide him with
the riotous entertainment he is accustomed to, but it would be
refreshing and different if you turned one of your gardens into
an aviary, with sweet-singing birds."

Impulsively, she went to him, clasped his arm and laid her
head on his shoulder. "Thank you, Olympus."

It took time to accomplish all she wanted. She kept her preparations as secret as possible, but all day long her apartments were
crowded with seamstresses, tailors, curtain-makers, painters,
cabinetmakers, artists and artisans of all kinds. A hundred new
gardeners were employed. Masons, tile-setters, bricklayers were
in and out of her rooms.

Even before her party, she taught herself to smile at her father
and laugh at his jokes. When she asked him to hear the petition
of this man or that one, he grumbled but agreed. Money came
easily to Cleopatra.

And, oddly, her mercenary motives brought her an unlooked-
for reward. Listening to the petitioners' troubles taught her things
about her own country she had not known before. A reservoir in
Upper Egypt needed to be repaired? She was puzzled. She wondered why reservoirs were necessary. A caravan traveling through
the desert had been taxed when they reached Memphis—did tax
collectors have this right? The papyrus reeds in Lake Mareotis

were growing too thickly, and the boats going to and from the Nile were becoming enmeshed in them. Should they not be cut down?

She caught a glimpse of the thousands of problems that could beset the ruler of such a country.

Great was the astonishment in the palace when announcement was made of an afternoon's entertainment in Princess Cleopatra's apartments. The tongues clacked loudly throughout the whole city. Some thought it was time for her to emerge into court society; some thought it presumption in one so young. All were curious and hoped for invitations.

When the afternoon arrived and she received her guests, their astonishment knew no bounds. Instead of the usual cool, chaste white rooms of Grecian art and architecture, with subdued lights and graceful pillars, these rooms were alive with color—reds, blues, greens, gold and silver—in the old Egyptian manner. Along the white walls were painted murals of Egyptian gods and kings and all phases of life—boats, rivers, trees and animals—in vivid colors. The figures were sharply etched in profile.

Golden lions in alabaster crouched holding up tables, chairs and couches. The Doric pillars had been painted over, in gold leaf and vermilion.

The lotus-flower and the papyrus motif were everywhere— carved in precious stones, outlined in enamel work, fashioned into cups and in jars where rare incense burned.

The floor of her anteroom had been painted to resemble a fish pond so that her guests marveled as they seemed to walk over the water. The painted reeds seemed to bend under their feet. The fish and ducks were so realistic that many guests bent down to touch and feel them.

Couches, chairs and benches were carved out of solid ivory. The cushions on them were of gold silk. One table was made entirely of lapis lazuli; another of malachite. The copper screen which Appolodorus had bought for her stood behind a great alabaster vase.

"How exotic! How bizarre!" the guests murmured.

Most sensational of all was the Princess herself. While the other women and girls came in long robes, gathered at the waist with crossed ribbons, Cleopatra was dressed in a tight sheath which covered her from above the breast straight to her ankles. It was tight and she was slim; in it she was a sculptured figure much like those of her wall paintings.

Her bronze-colored hair hung to her shoulders, curled in long ringlets, and over it she wore a diadem of gold, inset with green and red jewels. Around her neck was an extremely wide band which was also of gold and inset with pearls and rubies and green stones.

Since early morning she had been getting ready. She had been bathed and oiled. The manicurist and the chiropodist had been there. It had taken two hours to curl her hair, then her face was made up: green malachite eye shadow was applied to her upper lids and black kohl outlined the eyes and eyebrows to make them larger. Her nails were brushed with henna to pinken them and her lips painted with red.

"She is not as pretty as Arsinoë," Cleopatra heard one woman say, "but she does have distinction. An interesting face."

This they said when they thought she did not hear. Openly they said, "Dear little Princess Cleopatra, how charming you look. What a pleasure it is to feel the palace once more has a hostess! You have dazzled us all with this change; we must go home and redecorate in the Egyptian style. That copper screen— the Thos family must be eaten up with envy! The paintings are exquisite. I always thought of them as belonging in temples, not in homes, but of course a princess may do as she sees fit. . . ." On and on the voices babbled around her.

She kept herself aloof and dignified, although it was an effort. She was excited. When her father arrived, with his courtiers, she bowed to him and was pleased by his amazed delight. She conducted him, with all the guests trailing after, to the garden where thousands of birds in cages burst into song.

She did not have dancing girls or the kind of entertainers who sang doubtful jokes, but she did have a magician who was new to the palace and to Alexandria. Everyone was enchanted with the miracles he performed. He worked with birds, both live ones and toy ones, so that the whole afternoon seemed to be one of fairy enchantment.

It was suited to a young girl. The jaded appetites and tastes of the King and the Alexandrians were refreshed by it.

"I was wrong," Appolodorus whispered to her, "when I argued with you that this would be too tame and childish for them. They are enjoying the novelty of its innocence."

The party was a success. Auletes beamed upon her and called her his favorite daughter, his lotus flower, his jewel. Arsinoë burst into tears and had to be taken out by her tutor, Ganymede. Saat, one of the King's advisers, noted for his honesty and his stiff-necked pride, spoke to Cleopatra.

He was a member of one of the oldest and noblest Egyptian families who looked upon the Greeks as interlopers, but he said to her, "You do yourself and your country great credit, Princess Cleopatra, in rediscovering the charm of Egyptian art and style. It becomes you."

"I like it, my lord Saat," she replied. "While I am proud of the Greek culture I never forget that this is Egypt."

"Then may I take advantage of my years and venture a criticism? We Egyptians like color and richness but, while your rooms are lovely, they are a bit too colorful and too rich," he said.

She was almost angry, then she looked into his wise, steady eyes and she blushed. "I will learn, my lord Saat."

He patted her arm, and she knew she had made a good friend.

When her father and the other guests left, she was surprised to find that Pothinus and General Achillas, who was now general of all the army, lingered behind.

"May we have a word with you in private, Princess?" Achillas asked.

"Of course," she said, leading the way to chairs for them. She was puzzled. Neither of these two had ever paid her much attention, and all of Pothinus' interest had been centered on her brother. Both were ambitious men. What did they want of her?

Pothinus began, in his usual smooth, oily way. His fat face wore a subtle look, half-flattering, half-threatening. "We have remarked, Princess, that you are no longer a child. Nor are you the bookish girl who had such an odd liking for the company of scholars. You will soon be fifteen—almost a woman. Today you have displayed the woman's natural instinct for beautiful and costly objects and the woman's natural desire to be admired and envied. That is admirable. It is proper. Leave books and weighty subjects to others. Occupy the pedestal and be worshipped. Too much thinking only brings wrinkles to a woman's face. Leave the thinking to others."

"What others?" she watched him closely.

"To myself, for one. To General Achillas, for another. Let us be your friends. Let us guide you, plan for you, scheme for you, and when you are queen of Egypt we will take from your shoulders all that is annoying and worrisome to you. You must be free to amuse yourself."

He would have patted her hand with his thick, sausage-like fingers but she drew back. "What do you say, General Achillas?"

"I am a blunt soldier." His proud and haughty face made him a strange man to consort with one like Pothinus, yet the two were often together. "I command the army and the navy. Between the cleverness of Pothinus, who knows how to plan political strategy, and my power as general, your position as queen will be safe. We will guarantee it. You will be able to deck yourself with all the jewels you want and amuse yourself as you please. We will take care of the rest."

She was so furious she could not sit still, and got up and stood in front of them. "The price of my safety and my pleasures being that I become a puppet in your hands. I am to do your bidding. Is it not enough that you have my brother under your control, Pothinus? Must I, too, yield my will to yours? You will protect me, General Achillas, with your army—how dare you speak of it as yours! The army of Egypt is sworn to defend and obey the Ptolemies. Must I kneel to you for that defense? When I am queen I will rule, not you. Get out of my rooms!"

Achillas' face was purple-dark with anger. Pothinus had lost his smirk. There was poisonous hatred in the look he gave her as he left. "You will regret this, I warn you," he said, softly.

She had made two very powerful enemies. After they had gone she threw a cushion to the floor, seized a vase and smashed it in her anger. She paid no attention to the dozens of slaves who were straightening up her apartments after the guests had disarranged it, carrying out amphoras of wine and fruit juices and platters of half-eaten food. She realized that she had won one victory, in pleasing her father, and now she faced other and worse problems.

It had not been wise to anger those two men. Could she have helped it? Could she have smiled at them, knowing they meant to have her under their thumbs? At the thought of it, suddenly her own anger cooled, and she threw herself on a couch to think soberly.

She was too intelligent to let herself be managed by others. She was too proud to be flattered into complaisance, too self-willed to be guided in anything except small matters. Yet she would need friends. She would need advisers who would not try to control her. Where would she find them?

During the next two years she grew to understand a little but to be perplexed by much. Her father continued, in his careless way, to be pleased by her. Though he paid slight attention to any of his children, she was his favorite.

Yet she sensed that Auletes' power was hollow. Decisions were made in the council room without him. More and more she saw that Pothinus and Achillas were gathering about them a party of Alexandrians who would be devoted to her brother, as Ganymede and his group were devoted to Arsinoë.

Her own friends were not politicians. She made the mistake of not cultivating politicians; they bored her. She preferred the wise philosophy of Olympus or the exciting discoveries of Sosigenes or the light and amusing companionship of Appolodorus.

Saat tried to warn her. "Now is the time, Princess, when you should be carefully selecting those men who will make a strong party around you."

She was too young and too inexperienced to know how to go about it. She was too proud to let others do it for her. So those years drifted on. She changed, physically. She was no longer so thin. Her face developed a striking quality which some called beauty and others thought merely odd. Her eyes were large. Her nose was aquiline, but not the high, thin-boned type so much admired. Her chin had a suggestion of blunt strength which was offset by a mouth intensely feminine. Her two best features were her eyes, which changed expression with every mood, and her voice.

Young men were beginning to notice and court her.

Though she was growing up, physically, she was not maturing in wisdom. Time hung idly on her hands. She gave parties. She hoped in this way to make friends for herself, but she did not know how to flatter this man or listen to another or take sides with one against another, nor did she fathom all of the feuds and alliances that made up the strong and weak elements in the aristocracy.

Only her intelligence and her instincts kept her from appear-
ing a fool before these sophisticated people. Pothinus laid traps
for her. "Which religion do you prefer, Princess Cleopatra?" he
asked, once, in front of a roomful of people. "Do you hold with
the Greek gods or the Egyptian gods?"

In that room were both Greeks and Egyptians. It would be
easy to offend either. "Alexandria has long been famous for its
tolerance," she answered. "Many gods are tolerated and assimi-
lated. The Ptolemies were born Grecian; they have the protection
of Greek gods. But the Ptolemies have been adopted by Osiris,
by Isis and by Horus. We are their anointed."

So she avoided that trap, but she sometimes fell into others
and then she had to watch the smile on Pothinus' face, the satisfaction on General Achillas', and the gloating of her brother
and sister.

Suddenly, in the year 52 B.C., Auletes, Ptolemy XI, died.

The ceremonies of funeral for the King and the coronation of
both brother and sister were solemn and religious. At seventeen,
she took precedence over her ten-year-old brother, who was now
Ptolemy XII, and she went alone to the temple with the Egyptian
high priest and made offerings so that the Ka, the spirit, of her
father would not die but would continue to live. She was carried
through the streets on a golden litter for everyone to see, and she
was hailed in extravagant terms as the "Come-Back-to-Life of
Isis"—"Chosen of Ptah"—"Child of the Sun."

She and her brother ascended the twin thrones and each had
the double crown of Upper and Lower Egypt placed on their
heads.

She took it for granted that she would rule. Her brother was
only ten, still a child. He would be a king in name only until
he came of age.

One week after she was crowned Queen Cleopatra, the period
of deep mourning was considered finished. The pleasure-loving

Alexandrians demanded a celebration, so a chariot race in the stadium was arranged. It was their favorite sport. Cleopatra must be present to award the prize to the winner.

Olympus sat next to her. "You look the same as when you were just a princess," he said to her smiling. "Do you feel like a queen?"

"I'm trying to, but it doesn't seem real yet. I want so much to be a strong queen. I will never have people laugh at me as they laughed at my father," she said.

Olympus took no part in politics but he was a keen observer. "You will need to be strong and I think you will be. You resemble your earlier ancestors, the strong Ptolemies. Will you model yourself after them?"

"Yes, and after Alexander the Great. It seems to me, Olympus, that the most important thing is not ever to be afraid."

He pulled at his lip. "As a doctor, I can only advise you that a little bit of fear can be a good thing; it can make you cautious so that you do not run head first into danger."

The great race-course stadium was filled now with spectators who were wild with excitement over the promise of the day's sport. They were yelling for the races to start.

Olympus began to speak but he was interrupted. It was General Achillas.

"Queen Cleopatra," he bowed, a very short bow that was more mockery than sincere. "May I claim the privilege of this bench beside your chair?" A physician had not the stature of a general, and he must politely give way.

She could only say yes. Her brother, on the other side of her, was leaning forward, restlessly eager for the races, talking with animation to Pothinus. Cleopatra felt herself hemmed in by these three, with no friend near her.

To save herself the unpleasant necessity of speaking to them she looked across at the far stands. On her side of the stadium sat the nobility; on the opposite were the common people of Alexandria. It struck her that she knew nothing of them. She had never spoken to any of them, except to an artist or a craftsman on a special errand to the palace.

The first race started. The stands were full of screaming, delirious people, shouting encouragement.

If appearances counted for anything, she was every inch a queen; dignified when others around her behaved as if they were mad. She was trying hard. Let no one say she acted the clown, as they had said of Auletes!

Four more races went by; then came the major race of the day. Six of the finest chariots and drivers were entered. The stadium rocked with shouts and cheers. One chariot turned over. Horses and driver were badly hurt. Another lost a wheel on the third round. Then the winner came in.

As the hoarse cheers died down, the winner climbed out of his chariot and strode over to a position in front of the royal box. He held his head down, modestly, waiting for the laurel wreath to be put on it.

Cleopatra stretched out her hand for the wreath, but she was too late. As if by accident, Achillas had his hand on her arm, and was pulling at it saying at the same time, "See how handsome he is, Queen Cleopatra. Does he not touch your heart—forgive me, did I interfere with you?"

She jerked her hand loose and reached for the laurel wreath. It was gone. Pothinus had picked it up and placed it in her brother's hands. So it was Ptolemy XII, not Cleopatra, who rose to his feet to be applauded by everyone and be the center of all eyes as he advanced and placed the wreath on the winner's head.

"You did that on purpose, Achillas!" Gone was her dignity. She was spitting like a cat.

"Did what? Have I offended you?" He was smiling.

Now she knew that Olympus had been right. She would have

been wise to fear these two men. She was in danger. They were going to do their best to take the power away from her and use it to their best advantage through the boy-king. The clever trick they had worked just now was a sign of what she could expect. She was dazed. The crown on her head felt heavy.

THREE

SHE came to her first Council meeting, worried but determined. Saat was there. He would help her. She walked to the raised dais and took her seat in the chair of state which had been her father's. From this vantage point she looked over the twenty-five men who were present and wondered just how capable they were. They had advised Auletes on matters of finance, taxation, shipping, drainage of land and similar problems. She would have to learn for herself how well they could do their jobs.

"My lords," she began, "I am young but be not misled by that fact. I intend to rule justly and well. You must help me to understand the problems of government, in order that I may judge wisely."

She saw Saat nodding his iron-gray head with approval.

"You must not think that there is any question too difficult to explain simply because I am young or because of my sex. The long history of Egypt gives us many examples of great and wise queens—"

She was interrupted. The door opened and her brother came in, flanked on one side by Pothinus and on the other by Achillas. Ptolemy XII walked, without a word, to the chair next to hers and lounged back in it, arranging toy soldiers on the broad chair arm. Pothinus then said, "I am certain, Queen Cleopatra, that it was merely an oversight on your part that you forgot to consult with your brother, the King, about this meeting. Did you not even intend to notify him?"

There were frowns on the faces of some of the ministers. Others looked bewildered. Ptolemy XII had every right to be there—but was it the place for a boy of ten, playing with toys?

"If my brother wishes to take part in this Council, then let him speak," she demanded.

Ptolemy XII looked up at her and scowled. He muttered, "Pothinus will talk for me. He will look after my interests. And General Achillas is my friend." He dropped one of the clay soldiers and crawled under his chair to retrieve it.

They had tricked her neatly. She could not refuse to let her brother attend Council meetings. It was his right. She could not exclude those he wished to have speak for him. It was a farce, of course. Pothinus and Achillas were using a legal right only to get themselves on the Council where they would speak for themselves. Let the boy amuse himself here, rather than in his apartments—why not?

She was helpless to object to the proceedings. One of her advisers begged permission to speak of the problem of the Roman legions who had remained in Alexandria after General Gabinius had left. Many of the Roman soldiers had married Egyptian women. They seemed to have no desire to go back home, yet the royal treasury must pay them for doing nothing. Their swaggering manners offended the townspeople, and there had been some minor riots.

"What must we do? Request Rome that they be recalled? Cut off their pay? Or put up with their swaggerings and their insults?" he put the questions before the Council.

The Queen said, with some heat, "Why must we pay them to live here when they do nothing but insult our people, just because they are Romans?"

"May I speak?" It was Achillas. All fell silent. As general of the army he would be expected to know more on this subject than they. "Our Queen speaks from her heart and that is commendable. Her feelings are admirable. But are they wise? The pay of these legions is of no great sum. There is a copper screen in the Queen's apartments which cost more than three months' salary for all these Roman soldiers. Is it wise to offend Rome over such a trivial matter? When they are needed they will be recalled. In the meantime, let us not fall out with Caesar and Pompey over this. If there are any more disturbances my soldiers will handle them, quietly."

She bit her lip. Achillas was right. She saw heads nodding. Even Saat was impressed.

"So it shall be then, General Achillas," she decided. "*Our army shall protect the Alexandrians and punish the Romans if necessary.*"

The Council went on to other matters. The grain harvest had been poor that year along the upper Nile Valley. Relief was needed.

"There are ships full of grain in the harbor. Cannot they be taken up the Nile to prevent starvation?" asked Cleopatra.

Saat shook his head. "That grain is already sold and consigned to buyers. The money has been paid for it."

"If the Queen wishes the grain to go back to the Nile, it can be done," said Pothinus. "I think it a mistake to break faith with the purchasers, but who can deny that our Queen is thinking of the suffering of her people?"

So it was ordered. After the meeting Saat joined her, alone. His face was troubled. "Pothinus did you a bad turn, Queen Cleopatra, by supporting your wish to return the grain to the Nile. Some other method must be found to help the people until the next harvest. Wealthy landlords own that grain, not the people who live on the estates and who toil for it. Those landlords will raise an outcry when they hear what you have done.

They will say you rob them. You will make powerful enemies."

Warned in time, she countermanded her order. Saat discovered warehouses of corn not yet sold. These were paid for out of the royal treasury and sent to the people of the upper Nile.

She had been saved that blunder, but she made many more. Pothinus was a fox and Achillas was popular. They did their best to discredit her and maneuver her into making poor decisions. She knew now what their plan was. She was to become so disliked that when the boy-king was old enough to rule, Egypt would accept him. She would be pushed into the background. Queen Cleopatra would be a nobody.

She worked. She studied and learned the intricacies of politics and finance. Desperately, she struggled to challenge every move that Pothinus and Achillas made against her. Three years went by. When she was twenty, in the year of 49 B.C., she had achieved a great deal. She had won the confidence of most of her ministers, who were amazed that such a young woman could be so astute in business matters.

Appolodorus warned her. He lived the life of a young man of fashion, and he heard most of the gossip of Alexandria. "Achillas and Pothinus are worried. They have started ugly rumors about you and, unfortunately, many people are willing to believe them. You must be on guard."

The rumors spread. Queen Cleopatra was reported to give drunken orgies in the palace; to be so extravagant that her luxuries were ruining the country; to be so stingy in spending money that it showed a lack of respect for her position. The rumors contradicted each other but there was always someone ready to believe one story or another.

The most persistent were the tales of her scandalous conduct with young men. Her name was linked with Appolodorus and with many others, including handsome young slaves who worked in the palace. If she had been plain, the scandal might not have been so great. She had grown into a striking kind of beauty, so different that some would not even admit she was pretty. The vitality of her face and the animation of her eyes were not always admired by more passive women or by men who liked women to be passive creatures. Still, it was generally admitted that she had a potent attraction for young men. The scandalous rumors grew into fantastic proportions.

"Perhaps Appolodorus does give her the affection she needs so badly, poor little Queen." Iras was talking to Olympus as the two descended the stairway leading to the outside gardens. "Is that a crime? Would it not be unnatural if she did not seek love?" Cleopatra overheard the conversation from a window above them.

Olympus was a philosopher and a keen observer. "She is, by nature, passionate. Therefore the stories can be believed. She is also, by nature, discriminating and fastidious. Therefore she is not wanton. The stories are not to be believed. She is lonely but she is also very much occupied. So you see, Iras, it would be impossible to know the truth and our Queen has the rare ability to keep her own secrets. My own opinion is that it would be an unusual man to please such an unusual and brilliant woman as she."

Listening, Cleopatra's first reaction was one of disgust. Even her close friends gossiped about her. But at least they loved her and meant her no harm. She thought, sadly, of what they had said. Olympus was right; she was lonely.

She was of an age for love and courtship and marriage, but she had not yet met any man strong enough or clever enough to touch her deeper feelings. Appolodorus amused her and she was fond of him. She did not love him.

It was her brother's tutor, Theodotus, who spread the most damaging report of her. He claimed that it was because she had other lovers that she so obstinately refused to actually become the wife of Ptolemy XII. Ptolemy was now thirteen. Why did not Cleopatra recognize her duty to Egyptian law and live with him as man and wife? Was there to be no heir to the throne because she refused?

This disturbed even some of her faithful supporters. They might dislike the idea as much as she did, yet insist that she sacrifice her morals to the Ptolemaic conception of morality. There must be a son and heir.

Saat spoke to her, privately. "The situation is dangerous, Queen Cleopatra. Pothinus and Achillas are not the kind of men who would be content to go on matching wits with you. They will make a move—and soon. They have found they cannot use you, cannot bully or frighten you. Whatever plan they have, the groundwork has been laid with these scandals. I believe they are preparing people to accept your abdication as queen."

"If I will not abdicate, they are preparing people for my death." Her voice shook, "I know. I have seen the way Pothinus looks at me. Yesterday, my food taster died from a poisoned melon."

The food tasters were convicted criminals already sentenced to death. They welcomed the chance of escaping certain death by crucifixion for the less certain dangers of tasting all of the food before the royal family ate of it. Many lived out their natural lives; a few suffered the quicker death of poison instead of the lingering torture of their criminal sentence.

"Then be on guard. It is the only advice I can give you," said Saat. His lined face showed the anxiety he felt.

She must do more than just be on guard. She must get herself out of her enemies' hands. Once she was safe she could fight them.

A new play was to be given at the magnificent theatre next to the museum. Everyone in Alexandria who could afford it was going to the performance in the late afternoon. That morning the Queen summoned Saat and Appolodorus and Demetrius, her old teacher.

They came to her small office room, and each man bent his knee and his head. Each murmured, "Hail, Queen Cleopatra."

Appolodorus added, "Such charm and beauty as yours would be reason enough to bring me hither, but have you a command for me—"

She cut him short. "There is no time for pretty speeches, Appolodorus. The matter is crucial. There was another attempt to poison me, this morning."

Of them all, only Demetrius was astounded. He took no part in palace affairs. Cleopatra saw his expression and she leaned forward and put her hand on his arm.

"Rise, Demetrius. Be seated. I have called you together to ask your advice. Demetrius sees and is confided in by the more serious young men of Alexandria. He can tell of opinions outside our knowledge."

Now she whispered, "I must leave the palace and Alexandria. Egypt is large. From some other city I can denounce Pothinus and Achillas as traitors. I can publish the truth: that they only use my brother to take power themselves. I can appeal to my people to support their rightful queen."

Saat was nodding his head, vigorously. "Egypt is not just Alexandria, though Alexandrians like to think so. Achillas has the army but you will find the people loyal to you."

Appolodorus was excited. In emergencies he thought and acted well. It was only in times of inaction that he was bored and restless. "We have no time to be considering far into the future," he said. "We must plan for the immediate move. How shall we get you away safely? Let me think."

"I have already thought of a plan," she said. "But, first, let me ask Demetrius what he has heard of me. Do I stand completely discredited?"

"Of the young men in my charge," he spoke thoughtfully, "many belong to families who live in Memphis, Thebes or other towns. They care nothing for palace gossip. It is enough for them that you are your father's principal heir; you were named by him. You are older than your brother. These past three years have been without serious problems for them. Their land has prospered. They are confused by rumors but they have reason to believe you will be a good ruler."

Saat agreed. "They are already remarking the difference between you and your father and Berenice."

"This, then, is my plan." She spoke rapidly, keeping an eye on Charmian who was watching the doorway and hall. "Today I will attend the performance of the play. I will have a sudden headache and I will leave. None of you will go to the play. Wait for me at the royal pavilion, on the small island of Antirrhodos in the harbor. Make your way there as quietly as you can, in small boats. We will confer there. We will be safer there than here. If you know of anyone who can be trusted and whose help we need, bring him. Come prepared to make plans for my escape."

She saw the quick motion of Charmian's hand. She clapped her hands for a slave who immediately brought over the wine cups ready for this emergency. They were passed around. Cleopatra forced herself to smile and she sipped the wine.

Loudly, she said, "So you think we must buy these books from Pergamum? Their library is second to ours, but Pergamum is no longer an important town. Few people go there. Can we not exchange grain, which they need, for books which they do not?"

Demetrius had his back to the door, and he could not possibly see the quiet approach of Pothinus, but he was quick to take his cue from her words. As if they had been talking only of libraries, he laughed and said, "The people of Pergamum are as jealous of their library as if it were still a center of culture. I fear we must pay highly for the parchment scrolls we want. Oh, Pothinus, I did not see you approach—do you attend the play this afternoon? I fear it is a modern farce and not to be compared with the glorious Aristophanes."

Pothinus' suspicious eyes went from the bland face of De metrius, to Appolodorus, sprawling carelessly on a bench, to

Saat whose attention was, seemingly, taken by the pleasure of the wine he was drinking.

The suspicious eyes became mocking ones. "I see the Queen has never lost her admirable taste for scholarship. Forgive this intrusion. I came to inquire after the Queen's health. Are you feeling well?" he asked her, with a cruel meaning.

She hated him but it did not show in the steady gaze she turned on him. "I am well, Pothinus. You may rejoice at the news. If your friends or my brother are worried about my health, they may rejoice to know that I never felt better in my life."

That afternoon she was successful with her ruse. Halfway during the performance she was seen to put her hand to her forehead and moan piteously. She knew that Pothinus was delighted when she left the theatre; it meant another opportunity for the crowd to see her brother as king, alone, without her overshadowing presence.

She was concealed by a hooded cloak which Charmian had ready for her, and was rowed across to the island. In the beautiful marble pavilion, shaded by thick shrubs and trees from prying eyes, she found Saat and a young captain of troops, Appolodorus and a burly ship's captain, Demetrius and two young students of his.

They gathered around her. "You are brave men," she told them. "You will need to be still braver. I ask of you a hard thing: to believe that I do not intend to flee only for my safety but in order that I may better fight for my rights. I am queen by divine authority of the gods, yet I can only assert that right when I am secure from the threat of stealthy murder."

The two young students dropped to their knees. The others pressed around her, urging her to believe that they understood. The troop captain said, "If you go, Queen Cleopatra, Achillas will declare you a deserter of the throne and incite the army to capture you and bring you back. He has had soldiers killed for praising you."

"Let us strike first! Command," cried one hotheaded student, "that the household guards arrest Pothinus and Achillas when they return from the play."

"I do not know how many of the guards have been bribed and corrupted by him." Cleopatra shook her head. She smiled at the youth, and he looked as if he had won a great fortune.

Saat had been thinking and his older head was a wise one. "If the Queen leaves and makes her headquarters in a different place, then the issue becomes clear-cut. People will have time to choose without the turmoil there would be here if we tried to arrest either of these men. The Queen in one place, Pothinus and Achillas in another—that is the best way. The people will choose."

"You must go soon," Appolodorus said impatiently. "This ship's master has a swift galley. He can be ready for you day or night."

"Why wait? Even this night might be fatal." She spoke to the ship's master. "Can your fast ship sail now, while the play still goes on? I can be rowed, with Iras and Charmian, from this very pavilion. Appolodorus can go with us. Saat, your name is so respected that not even Pothinus would dare avenge his anger on you. Stay here and look to our interests. Demetrius, speak to every student who has ever done military service or driven a chariot or ridden a horse for sport. Tell them to join me at Pelesium."

The sea captain was protesting, but the army man spoke first. "My troops are equipped and ready to move. I shall march them out before Achillas discovers you are gone. He will charge me with treason but it is he who is traitor!" His eyes flashed.

At last the seaman could speak. "Your gowns, Queen Cleopatra, your servants, your furnishings—you will need them. There are no provisions on board my cargo ship for any woman, let alone a queen. It would be a terrible ordeal, with no comforts for you."

"I can sustain a few hardships. Rest easy; I will not complain. Come." She walked down to the steps where a rowboat waited.

Its two oarsmen were from the ship. "Is there room in that boat for all of us? Then let us go."

They had all turned to follow her when they heard, from back in the trees, a high and gleeful laugh. Startled, they looked up. The hands of the troop captain and the young men went to their short swords in their belts.

Arsinoë stepped from behind the shelter of the trees, still laughing. When she could speak she said, "You need not fear me. Put up your swords. I will not stop my dear, elder sister from running away. It suits my purpose that you go and that people say you are nothing but a frightened girl. You will die in some obscure place or be brought back here in chains."

"And you will marry our brother and be queen. No, I do not fear you, Arsinoë, because you have a reputation for telling lies. Remain here, in the company of these handsome students, for a few hours. You would let me escape, Arsinoë, for your own schemes, but it occurs to me that you could not keep your hands from my jewels. Charmian, go back to the palace and bring them to the ship. We will need them to pay those who fight for us. Saat, do not worry what she might say after I am gone. No one would believe her word against yours."

The ship sailed, unobtrusively, within the hour. No one on shore marked its going. No alarm was given.

The voyage to Pelesium, eastward along the coast, was the first physical hardship Cleopatra had ever endured. She could hardly believe that human beings lived without silken sheets or perfumed baths. When she found there were no sheets at all, just coverings over straw mattresses laid on a wooden bunk, and that instead of her sunken tub of hot water she must wash her face in cold, salt water, she was shocked.

But this was the ordinary life of seamen, and she had given her word to the captain that she would not complain. When Iras and Charmian whimpered she scolded them, "You are silly girls.

Would you rather stay in Alexandria and be put to torture after my death?"

"Could any torture be worse," Charmian moaned, "than straw sticking me in the back all night long?"

They found the town of Pelesium quiet and sleepy. Cleopatra and Appolodorus had two days in which to inspect the fort, to the great amazement of the soldiers stationed there. When the situation was told to them they immediately declared themselves loyal to her. They were her first troops.

The fort, Appolodorus declared, was of no value to them. "It will not do. We cannot defend it. Until we know whether we have many soldiers or few, we should not attempt to hold out against a siege, nor should we attempt a pitched battle." Like most wealthy young men Appolodorus had served time as a young officer and had studied military strategy. "We must get horses. A small force that can move fast can outmaneuver Achillas' foot soldiers."

They spent lavishly in those two days, buying fast horses and camels. The troop captain joined them on the third day. He had quick-marched overland and brought every soldier he could. He reported that Achillas was already preparing to move his whole army against her.

"We were half a day out of Alexandria when a messenger brought us the news that you had successfully escaped. It is said that the rage of Achillas and Pothinus was awful. You had slipped through their fingers. They swear to capture you and bring you before your brother for judgment—and death."

He approved the plans Appolodorus had made. "We have not enough men to fight Achillas' army. We will delay here just long enough for him to think he will have an easy victory; then we ride off and gather more forces as we go inland."

This was exactly what happened. The Queen's forces defended the fort and town just long enough for Achillas to think they had settled in for a siege. He put his men into encampment and sat down to starve out and drive out the Queen. At that moment she and her several hundred troops, all mounted, fled again. They were guided at night through the marshy lands by an Egyptian who knew the trails of firm ground.

Iras and Charmian had been sent on two days earlier. Now, through the long night and all the next day, Cleopatra rode in a growing numbness of body. She was beaten by fatigue, pounded by pain and aches. Finally, only the strength of her will kept her from fainting.

The next day was worse. But by the third day she had become slightly accustomed to it; her young muscles began to harden; the motion of the horse was less of a strain. At the first village they slept and refreshed themselves, but they were off again, with a few recruits to their army, before the pursuit could catch up to them.

She found the towns and villages wholeheartedly loyal to her, but they had few trained soldiers for her. She was advised by one wise town mayor: "Go to the desert, Queen Cleopatra—go there and find the tribesmen. They are fighters by tradition and practice. They are fierce. They do not till the soil as we do. We will keep you in food and supplies. The desert will be safe for you. Your army can operate from there."

Only much later did she realize how good this advice had been —it probably saved her. She had done a foolhardy thing in rushing out of Alexandria without knowing where or when her support would come. Fortunately for her, she turned her army to the desert which bordered the east of the Nile Valley.

Here she found the tribal chiefs. Dark-skinned, tall, hawk-faced, violent men they were, who knew every inch of desert, every oasis in this land. They rode their camels swiftly and tirelessly. They fought fanatically. They became utterly devoted to her, both as Queen and as a woman of courage. What captured them from the very beginning was the fact that she spoke their language. They were Egyptians but they knew nothing of Greek or Latin. Their own tongue was strange to most scholars even; it seemed wonderful that this beautiful queen should know it.

Once she was in the desert, Achillas developed caution. He constantly sent large bodies of men after her, but they had instructions to withdraw if the tribesmen rode as if to surround them. Achillas could afford to play a waiting game.

For a year and a half he kept her on the desert. He had too large a force to be dislodged without a massive attack. She did not have that kind of army. Her horsemen and her camel riders swooped down upon Achillas' sleeping soldiers. Men were killed; horses, supplies and prisoners taken. Then the phantom army melted away again in the darkness. Only the pounding of hoofs were left for Achillas to curse.

If he kept her from returning to her palace, she kept him and Pothinus and her brother from complete victory. The country was in the grip of civil war. No matter how many pronouncements came from the palace that there was no longer a queen, but a fugitive rebel named Cleopatra, the country knew better.

Ruler without a throne, she became also a fighter and a military leader. She applied the brilliance of her mind, immature as it was, to the study of tactics and strategy. When the army went out on raids or patrols she rode with them, dressed as a man, with a thin coat-of-mail specially made for her over her tunic.

She and her two maids lived in tents scarcely better than the coarse goat's-hair ones that sheltered her soldiers. She ate their food and suffered thirst on long rides, as they did. She took her place in councils with the desert chiefs and her officers, not by virtue of her title but because she earned that place.

Her training for leadership had begun in the palace. It had taken a strange turn, but she found that warfare developed in her the necessary abilities to make decisions carefully, change them with lightning speed when the situation demanded change, and search for imagination and wisdom in the men around her.

She was tougher than her small, slim body appeared to be.

Her muscles hardened. Her courage was determined in battle. Her imperious will found an outlet in simple, direct action.

Appolodorus, too, had changed. He said to her one day, as they talked outside her tent, "Two years ago I was composing verses to you, Cleopatra. Now that I could indeed write how glorious and valiant you are, alas! I can no longer scribble verse. My mind is too full of words of war to think of words to say how lovely you are—"

"Enough! Can anyone call me lovely? With my skin reddened and roughened by the sun and the wind? Look at my hands." She held them out. The palms had hard calluses from holding the reins of fast-running horses. "It doesn't matter. Nothing matters but that my spirit rebels at these endless months with nothing resolved. Pothinus sits in the Council and makes laws. My brother is on the throne. The Roman Senate has given him recognition."

"That means little. The Senate has no power. Only Caesar or Pompey could intervene in our affairs. Pothinus has merely bribed some insignificant Roman senator to get up in the Forum and make a motion. It doesn't change the situation," Appolodorus said.

"I know. What worries me is that we have had no news for two weeks—no, three weeks! Achillas has been successful in capturing our couriers. The last we heard was that Ptolemy was issuing reports that I was dead. There was also some news that those two Romans—Caesar and Pompey—had quarreled and become enemies. So there may be civil war in Rome as well as in Egypt." Arms crossed, her browned hands gripping her elbows, her heat bent, she paced up and down, thinking and talking.

Appolodorus raised his eyebrows. "I have sometimes thought you were almost content with this life and had no desire to return to Alexandria—don't be angry. I was merely jesting. I have heard you at the tribesmen's campfires, laughing with them and listening to their stories. What you find to say to them I do not know. I cannot understand a word they say."

She smiled at him. "They think you strange. They do not believe that you and they belong to the same country. I have learned much, Appolodorus. I shall never again think only of Alexandria when I think of Egypt. The Nile Valley and this desert have nothing to do with libraries and theatres." She stopped pacing and stood still.

Her ears had caught the sound of camels long before the six desert riders came into view. She waited for them. She saw, with excitement, that they had with them a stranger, a prisoner who was bound with cords to his saddle.

"We bring a prisoner and news, Queen Cleopatra," said their leader, dismounting. "He is a lieutenant of Achillas', and he has with him messages from Pothinus to Achillas." He handed the Queen some papers. "We could not read them."

She could, rapidly. She exclaimed, "There has been a battle at Pharsalus in Greece. It was a battle between Caesar and Pompey, and it is Pompey who was defeated." She stopped speaking and read on. When she raised her face it was agitated. "Call together all of the chiefs and head men for a conference this evening!" She changed to Greek and addressed the officers: "I have received important information which may change everything. I call a council this evening at sundown."

Around the campfire they gathered that evening. She stood inside the circle and told them, in both languages, of the terrible battle which had at last determined who was the strongest man of Rome. It was Julius Caesar.

The desert seemed far away from Rome or a battlefield in Greece. The men sat and listened to her. The firelight flickered on their upturned faces and on her coppery-brown hair, caught the glowing lights in her eyes. Some of her excitement communicated itself to the men. They shifted in their positions but they watched and listened intently.

"Pompey fled," she was speaking the language of the desert, then changing to Greek. "Pompey came to us, to Egypt for sanctuary. His ship anchored outside Pelesium. He was brought in a rowboat to the wharf. Pothinus stood on the harbor steps, waiting for the great man to approach and when Pompey did—when he stepped out of the boat onto the steps—Pothinus had two men grab him. Pompey was killed and his head cut off. Pothinus plans to give the head of Pompey to Caesar to win Caesar's favor."

There was a general murmur around the fire. Cleopatra heard their murmurs.

"Why do you feel pleased?" asked Appolodorus. "Was this not a clever and ruthless stroke? Pothinus will win the approval of Caesar, who is certain to follow and must be coming to Egypt at any moment. If Caesar is given the head of Pompey he must surely be grateful to Pothinus."

"That," said Cleopatra, her voice ringing out, "is where you are wrong. That is the great mistake which Pothinus has made and which is so serious it will put me back on the throne. Julius Caesar will be furious at this act of Pothinus!"

FOUR

THEY DID NOT believe her. The men from Alexandria were completely incredulous. The tribesmen looked puzzled.

She explained, "When I first became queen I understood little of these Romans. I will tell you a story. There were Roman soldiers left in Alexandria when General Gabinius left. The new Roman proconsul of Syria sent his son to Alexandria to round up these soldiers and take them back to active duty. They had found our country a pleasant place to stay, and they did not want to leave. Many had married Egyptian wives."

She was a vivid storyteller. "The proconsul's son arrived, a young man, the beloved of his father. These Roman soldiers refused to go with him to duty. They became angered. They murdered that boy. When I was told of the ghastly deed I had the murderers apprehended and tried for their crimes. The sentence of death was passed on them. I did not carry it out; I sent them back to Syria in chains to the proconsul."

Pausing, she waited to be sure of their full attention. "Do you think that proconsul was grateful to me? Do you think he thanked me for arresting the murderers of his son? He was indignant. He sent me a furious letter. By what right, he arrogantly demanded, did Egyptians arrest Romans? By what right did an

61

Egyptian court pass sentence on free Roman citizens? How did I dare to put chains on them!"

The other officers were amazed but the tribal chiefs nodded their heads. It was so with them. "Not even in the name of justice does one tribe touch a member of another, without being avenged," one told her.

"Do you understand?" Cleopatra turned to the rest. "Pompey came from one of the noblest families of Rome. He was once the greatest general. If he were killed in battle by Julius Caesar, whose family and reputation is as great as Pompey's was, then there would be no dishonor. If Pompey knew he were defeated with no chance to fight again, he would have the right to fall upon his own sword, by their code of honor. But what has Pothinus done? He has dared to lay hands on Pompey! A fat, greasy politician of lowly Greek birth has dared to strike off the head of a highborn Roman. He has snatched away Caesar's victory and glory. He has made Caesar's prize nothing but a dishonored humiliation."

They understood at last. "Caesar will be in Alexandria soon. If only we could be there, we could take advantage of this moment," said one of her lieutenants.

Appolodorus made the obvious answer to that. "The army of Achillas stands between us and Alexandria. We must send a message to Caesar. We must smuggle in a letter to him, setting forth your claims, Cleopatra."

One of the chiefs lifted his head and made a motion with his hand. Everyone was silent, waiting. The tribesmen rarely spoke. Only when it was important did they raise their voices.

"Egypt"—for so the desert men addressed her, instead of saying "Cleopatra"—"I do not know how it is with you who live in cities or with these Romans, but with my people there are times for truces and parleys. Quarrels are called off. Chiefs walk in safety with each other. They speak. If the quarrel can be settled, all is peace. If it cannot, then the chiefs return in safety to their tribes. Not until then does the fighting begin again."

Cleopatra had to explain to them that Achillas' hatred of her was so great that he would not agree, under any circumstances, to allow her to go unmolested through his lines. In fact, they would do everything they could to keep her and Caesar apart.

The meeting adjourned. There seemed to be no solution.

She was wakeful that night. Inside her tent she reclined on a hard couch covered with a tiger skin, using her saddle for a headrest. She had not taken off her cloak. The desert night air was cold. She shivered now and then, but her mind was too busy to take note of discomfort.

How could her army take her to Alexandria? Was this the moment to risk everything on a battle to drive through Achillas' lines? It was not. Her tribesmen were not foot soldiers. They were not equipped with helmets, shields and iron jackets for the slow, hand-to-hand fighting required to push an enemy back mile after mile.

She dismissed that thought and took up another. What kind of a man was this Julius Caesar? He had once named her father as an ally of Rome, but that was a political maneuver. Very likely he would now see, in the chaotic condition of Egypt, the perfect chance to step in and take the country as a province. Both she and her brother would be deposed.

Or he might decide to keep Ptolemy XII on the throne as a puppet. Was he shrewd enough to see that Pothinus' ambitions had swollen to such a degree that he would tolerate no interference from anyone?

All she knew of Caesar was that he had had a phenomenal rise to supremacy. Ten years ago his name had scarcely been mentioned. Then news had trickled into Alexandria: he was named consul and general. He had conquered great territories in strange places named Gaul and Spain, Germany and Britain. His legions were said to love him as no general had ever been loved before.

He was past middle age. He was married to his third wife. He was statesman as well as soldier, but he was not on good terms with the men of the Roman Senate.

That Senate had approved the kingship of her brother. Was that a point in her favor? She tried to think how Caesar, visiting Alexandria and hearing stories about her, would consider her position.

The picture drawn for him by Pothinus would not be a pretty one. She would be called a fugitive; a deposed queen, with no strong political party behind her; a girl who had lived a scandalous life in the palace; a young woman who was no better than a wild desert creature now.

She shivered again and clapped her hands. A servant who had been crouched, half-asleep, by a brazier of burning coals brought her a steaming bowl of mutton broth. Cleopatra warmed her hands around the bowl and sipped at the thick, fatty liquid.

All she had in her favor, really, was Pothinus' mistake. If Caesar were angry at this he would be emotional. If she could only see him while he was still emotional, it might tip the scales for her.

Her mind kept slipping away to the tantalizing suggestion of the tribal chieftain. It was what she wanted: a parley between herself and Caesar. It was foolish to think about it. Achillas would never permit a truce to allow her to come through his lines in safety—

She sat up suddenly. Achillas would not permit it, but suppose she slipped through without his knowledge?

"Go swiftly," she commanded the servant. "Arouse my lord Appolodorus. Bring him here at once."

Appolodorus was sleepy and cross when he came. "Must it be now? Cannot it wait until the morning, Cleopatra? I was just dreaming that I was entering a tavern on the Street of Canopus and the innkeeper was about to bring a platter of sturgeon—"

"This cannot wait." She unfolded her plan. Instantly he was wide awake and fully in agreement.

"Tell no one," she warned. "Not even Iras or Charmian must know. We will need the help of only a few men. Let everyone think I go to Pelesium to confer secretly there with some of our supporters, and that I will return. You must go tomorrow, Appolodorus, to find the brother of Saat, the one who lives near Memphis. Send him immediately to Saat in Alexandria. In four days you will meet me at Pelesium, in the Temple of Neptune. No one goes there; it is in ruins." For hours they discussed every single details of the plan. Rash and bold as it was, it might work.

In four days she was in the Temple of Neptune where Appolodorus was waiting for her. She had used her four days well. A rowboat was hidden. She and Appolodorus climbed into it. The oars were muffled; they slid undetected past the harbor guards. Pelesium was in the hands of Achillas, but there were few soldiers there now that Pothinus had departed after the slaying of Pompey.

From the rowboat she and Appolodorus were taken aboard a small Syrian trading vessel. The captain had been lavishly paid and was willing to run the risk.

A few nights later, the ship came slowly and inconspicuously into the Royal Harbor of Alexandria, past the giant marble lighthouse of Pharos. Both Cleopatra and Appolodorus, hidden below decks, looked out at it through a small opening with tears of homesickness in their eyes. This lighthouse, five hundred feet high, was the beacon they had known since childhood. It meant home to them; the world they had not seen for so long.

Familiar to them, also, was the glimpse they had of white stone buildings on the city side. It was too dark to see well, but they recognized the museum, the library and the theatre. The sounds of pipe and flute coming from the streets made them nostalgic. "I can hear the wheels of a chariot on the paving stones," whispered Appolodorus.

"I can smell the spices and fruits and leather, from the warehouses," she whispered in return.

Now she found herself trembling with the suspense. It was too late to turn back; she was afraid to go forward. Would the message have come to Saat? Perhaps he no longer cared to endanger his life for her. Perhaps—

Then she was being cautiously lowered into a tiny cockleshell of a boat and it was no use being afraid. She would have to go through with it. Appolodorus remained on board the ship.

The tiny boat was so small that no palace guard could see it in the darkness. It bobbed over the gentle waves and slid lightly down others. Before she knew it they had reached their destination: a flight of steps on the Lochias Promontory. These steps had not been used for years. They were overgrown with weeds and piled high with driftwood and refuse from the harbor.

She made her way up the steps alone. The boatman had been sent back. She would either succeed in this venture or be captured; there was no other way. Driftwood rolled under her feet and she fell twice, skinning her knees and tearing both cloak and tunic. Wet seaweed clung to her sandals. Tar and pitch stained her hands and clothes.

She gained the top and turned to the left, making her way carefully in the darkness. The palace wall was at her right and sometimes she felt along it with her hands to keep from stumbling. She was searching for a gate which was boarded up and abandoned. It must be near. Had she missed it in the darkness?

A hand touched her arm. A figure loomed up directly in front of her. She stifled a scream. It was Saat.

He dropped to one knee in the dirt and kissed her hand. Tears dropped and wet her fingers. "At last," he said. "You have come at last. I have been here at this hour the past two nights, Queen Cleopatra."

"You ventured so much? It is death and torture for you if my plan fails, Saat," she said.

He looked at her reproachfully. "It cannot fail. Osiris will not any longer tolerate that a toad like Pothinus should rule this country. I consulted the temple priest. All the omens are favorable."

She had not his trusting faith. She had only her courage. "Let us hurry. Is Pothinus in the palace?"

"There is a banquet in the great hall tonight. They will all be there—Pothinus, Ptolemy, Arsinoë and the ministers—to celebrate Caesar's visit here. Come," he said. He was getting old and he tottered in front of her to the gate. "Nobody notices what I do. Nobody has cared that I have wandered through the palace gardens in this direction, or noticed that I had tools and oil to fix this gate." It turned noiselessly under his hand, and they slipped through quietly.

A giant of a man waited for them on the other side. "It is only my slave," said Saat hurriedly as he felt her recoil. "It is my slave, Res, who will carry you."

"Carry me? How?" she asked.

"Everyone," he explained, "has given gifts to Caesar. All day and in the evenings slaves go to his chambers carrying presents from rich noblemen or merchants wanting favors from him. No one will think it strange that Res walks through the halls to Caesar's door, carrying a rolled-up, priceless rug from Persia, the gift of old Saat!"

On the ground at her feet she saw the rug spread out. For one second she was horrified. Then she realized the beauty of the plan. "You have been clever, my friend," she said. She clasped him in a quick embrace, too moved to say more.

She knelt down and stretched herself flat on the rug. With a skillful motion Res rolled her up in it. With one easy toss of his giant arms he got the rug over his shoulder, with the Queen rolled up inside it.

She struggled to get her breath. The folds were thick. Suffocation frightened her. She wanted to scream as the rug pressed against her face. Her hands were bound tight at her sides. Panic would have ruined everything; she fought it down and became calmer. If she didn't try to move she could get enough air.

Even through the thickness she could hear the crunch of Res' feet on the garden paths. She could tell from the tilt of her body when he left the garden and walked up steps to enter the palace. Once inside, she strained to try to tell where they were. Every sound was muffled: the scraping of sandals as servants passed; a hoarse growl of a steward berating a slave; the opening and closing of a door.

Res went swiftly. She could hear, faint at first and growing louder, the noise of the banquet hall. There was music and laughter and loud talk.

From this point on she was in mortal peril. If Res allowed the rug to slip, or if he were challenged to show what he carried, or if some drunken reveler bumped into them and felt that the rug was not as it should be, she would be discovered. She might be killed before Caesar even knew of her presence in the palace.

They passed the banquet hall safely. The music grew fainter. The rapid turnings and twistings, as Res made his way along, puzzled her. In what part of the palace were Caesar's apartments? They crossed a courtyard.

They were challenged: "Halt! What is your business here?"

The perspiration broke out on her face. Her heart clamored against her ribs. Suddenly she realized with joy, the challenge had been made in Latin and not in Greek. They must be at Caesar's door, and this sentry must be one of his own soldiers.

She heard Res explaining, in poor Latin, that he had a gift from the nobleman Saat to the great Julius Caesar. Her mind now had to worry about what would happen if the sentry refused admittance. It was equally difficult to imagine what would happen if the rug was carried in. Caesar's servants might arouse the whole palace when she was found in it. Just the same, if she did get in she would hardly be killed before she could see him.

The sentry must have stepped aside. His voice came from her left. Res was moving again. A door opened. She was carried into a quiet, quiet room. All she could hear was the rustle of papers. Then a voice spoke, firm and commanding: "What is this? I gave orders I was not to be disturbed."

She felt herself lowered to the floor and the rug unwound from her body. She heard the gasp of surprise from the unknown man. She crouched there for a fraction of a second to get her balance, then she rose to her feet, trying to stand as tall and regal as was possible under the circumstances. Her chin lifted. She looked straight into the eyes of Julius Caesar.

It could only be he. No one else would be in his apartments, sitting at ease before a desk, wearing the purple stripe of nobility on his white toga. Not only that, but the man himself was of such manner and authority it could only be Caesar.

He frowned. "A most unusual entrance, girl. If this is another one of Pothinus' ideas, I do not care for it. Does he send me a dancing girl rolled up in a carpet? Is this one of his sly insults— to send me a wench uncombed, dirty, ragged, smelling of tar and pitch and salt brine and"—he lifted a corner of her cloak and held it to his nose—"yes, smelling of the saddle? Go back and tell him Caesar wants none of his—" he broke off.

He stepped closer and looked at her face. He lifted the hair off her brow and studied her. "You are no dancing girl. Who are you?"

"I am Cleopatra, Queen of Egypt. I have come to you, Julius Caesar, to appeal for justice. Yes, my cloak smells of the saddle, because I, too, have had to become a warrior and ride and fight for my throne. I am covered with pitch and tar because I was forced to crawl through refuse to get to the palace undiscovered. The sea brine will tell you I came here by ship. My rough hands show you what I have endured and suffered, rather than bend my neck to Pothinus' yoke." Her voice rang clear.

"My entrance was unceremonious. It was not meant to amuse

you. It was the only way I could safely reach you. My friends and
this slave, Res, have risked their lives to bring me here."

He took her small hand and turned it over and looked at the
hard palm with its calluses. He frowned. "I have been told you
live a wanton, pleasure-loving life. I do not think you got such
marks as these on your hands from playing the harp. I have been
told you were a coward and deserted your people. Your way of
coming here tells me that you are, instead, bold and audacious."
His face was like granite but he said, gravely, "I greet Queen
Cleopatra."

Her heart gave a bound of painful hope. He had acknowledged
her and her title.

For the first time she dared to breathe. She looked at him and
saw a remarkable man. He was of middle height, but he carried
himself with such stature that he seemed taller. The white toga
fell in folds from one shoulder, leaving the other one bare. It had
the corded, scarred muscles of a man who had survived furious
battles. The face was haughty, cold and expressionless. His hair
was close-cropped in the Roman fashion, with a few strands curl-
ing on his forehead. A prominent nose and an iron-firm mouth
were the only outstanding features in his bronzed and weathered
face.

It was a face she could trust. He might not like her, she felt,
but he would be fair.

"And I greet the noble Caesar," she said to him. "I come to
you, a proud petitioner. I ask your help. I was named in my
father's will to succeed him, jointly with my brother. Pothinus
and Achillas control him. They wanted to control me. When I
refused they spread lies about me. My life was threatened and I
had to flee. But I have not deserted. My army has fought and
I have fought. The people are loyal to me, but Achillas controls
the mercenary soldiers who are paid to fight and care not for
whom they fight."

He nodded his head, but he asked coldly, "Why did you not rule in peace with your brother? You are the older."

She answered in only one word, gambling that he already knew and disliked what she would say: "*Pothinus.*"

He walked away from her and stood looking down at his desk. He touched a paper with his hand, then he suddenly swung around and faced her. "Did you say there was a will of your father? Does this still exist? A document is necessary. If your father named you as his heir, then that is the law. I uphold the law. I would insist upon your rights."

Joyfully, she smiled. "There is a will. I hid it before I left."

"It must be found. Neither Pothinus nor your brother said anything about a will. They said it was custom for brother and sister to occupy the throne—unless one proved unworthy as they say you have. Where is it?" He made it a demand, not a question.

"If Res"—she indicated the giant slave who had been silent and still all this time—"could go with one of your officers to the small garden opposite the golden gallery, at the end of the promenade of stone lions, he could dig under the largest palm tree in that garden and there he would find the box with the will in it."

Both Res and an orderly were dispatched on this errand.

Caesar seated himself and politely motioned her to a chair. "What do you ask of me, Queen Cleopatra?"

"Eventually, my lord, I ask your help in securing my throne, but at this moment I crave another boon of you," she said.

"What is that?"

She blurted out: "A bath! I stink of dirt. I crawl with lice from the ship I came on. I ache from fatigue."

His face softened. His lips twitched. "Forgive me. I am a poor host. We talked of the queen and forgot the woman. You will stay here tonight. I prefer to keep your presence a secret for the time. They have given me more rooms than I need; one shall be yours. I will have my servant bring a woman to attend you—"

"If your servant could also find the royal steward of the wardrobe perhaps he could procure for me some dresses of Arsinoë's. I am sure mine have been sold or given away." The thought of fine linens and silks made her realize how long she had gone without luxuries.

"It shall be done. That steward will only think I entertain a lady to whom I wish to make a present of a gown. It does not matter what he thinks." Caesar was almost fatherly as he gave her his hand and led her to an inner room. "You must rest. Later, perhaps, you will join me in a small supper?"

"Thank you. And perhaps when I am bathed and gowned you will think me more a queen and less like some wildcat," she said.

He bowed and took her hand. Once more he looked at her. "I like you well this way. You are a brave girl. If you had come to me dressed in silk, perfumed and soft and pampered, I should not have admired you as I do now." Suddenly his frosty eyes had real warmth in them and he exclaimed: "What a daring thing that was! To slip through all their lines and come before me rolled up in a rug. It was an act worthy of a Roman, and I can give you no higher praise than that."

Two hours later he was bent over a table, studying the will of Auletes, Ptolemy XI, when she called to him from the doorway. His face showed his amazement as he looked at her. The rough soldier-girl had disappeared. The ragged, tattered and dirty wench was gone. In place of her was a strikingly beautiful woman.

She was not tall, but slim and straight. Her thick hair was brushed and sleek and bound with a silver band across her forehead. Skillfully darkened, her long, arched eyebrows emphasized eyes so large and intense that they were magnetic. Her skin had been creamed and then washed in a special way which already had softened it. She was scented, jeweled and altogether lovely.

"I am a man not easily surprised," he said. "You have given me two, Queen Cleopatra. First you arose at my feet out of a rug, now you enter like a regal figure of beauty. Are you sure that the charge against you, of being a sorceress, is not true?"

"I suffered for this change!" She was laughing and her face was glowing. "The woman had to comb so hard that tears came to my eyes. She had to take pumice stone to the roughness of my elbows and the soles of my feet. See?" She extended one pretty, arched foot, bare in its sandal.

"Are you perchance attempting to win me to your cause by such attractions?" He retreated into severity.

But she was no longer awed by him. "I would if I could, Caesar, but I have lived a rough life so long, I am fearfully out of practice in attracting men."

"Then I must play the gallant and tell you that when you first spoke, when you were still dirty and ragged, you had one attraction that would fascinate any man—your voice. I have never heard one like it."

She caught sight of the papyrus scroll on his desk and dropped her playful manner. "It is the will. You have read it? Then you must know I spoke the truth."

There was a long pause while Caesar's eyes were stern upon her. "I will uphold your right. I have determined upon it. It will cause difficulties when I would prefer to finish my business in Alexandria quickly, and be off to Rome. Yet justice demands that you be reinstated as queen."

"Thank you." Tears glistened in her eyes and fell down her cheeks. It had been so long and so hard, this time of her exile. "I honor you, Julius Caesar, as my friend and patron. Queen Cleopatra will always be a friend to you, and Egypt a faithful ally to Rome." She went slowly over to a chair near him and sat down. Her head drooped. "I fear there won't be much of me to uphold unless you feed me. By Isis, my hosts in the desert at least offered me mutton broth and a camel haunch to chew on."

Then Caesar laughed, throwing back his head. "You are a creature of moods, Queen Cleopatra. I never know if I am speaking to the injured queen or the hungry girl." He spoke to his servant and platters of food were brought in. Then he said to

Cleopatra, "Tell me, honestly, did you eat such food? I've gone for days with nothing but rotten fish, but I am a soldier and I expect such hardships. Do you not exaggerate?"

"I? Not a word. It is the truth. Sometimes we rode for days with nothing but a handful of dates and a swallow of goat's milk to live on."

"Have you ever eaten bark? Why, when my legions crossed the Rhine we—" and he launched on an account of his own battles. She let him talk. She knew that he was enjoying her company, but it was an added pleasure for him to find a woman with whom he could talk of military matters.

When he spoke of Britain, she boasted of forays at night against Achillas. When he talked of the strange people he had met on his conquests, she could talk of her favorite desert tribesman. He seemed to like hearing these tales as much as he did recounting his own.

When she was at last in her silken bed, Cleopatra looked at her rough, red hands against the white sheets and admired them. They had done far more for her than she could have believed.

The next morning he told her that he had sent word to Pothinus that Caesar wished to meet with the King and his ministers that morning at ten o'clock. He requested that she be ready to accompany him at that time.

"Is General Achillas in Alexandria?" She was eating melon and figs but without appetite. Conflicting emotions upset her nerves. She was half-exulting over the coming discomfiture of her enemies; she was half-anxious because of the difficulties still ahead.

"No," Caesar told her, "but Achillas is coming. Pothinus has sent for him, I think." He was no longer smiling or relaxed as he had been the night before. Now he was careworn. "Pothinus, I am afraid, expected me to be more grateful than I am for the slaying of Pompey. Pothinus does not understand a Roman's attitude toward an honorable, fallen foe. I was to have been grateful and willing to support the King—and withdrew speedily from Alexandria. I made a reasonable request for gold. I cannot go back to Rome empty-handed. He haggles with me." Caesar's face darkened. "And he begrudges food for my soldiers and gives them poor and scanty corn."

"It was a shocking thing for a creature like Pothinus to lay hands on a man like Pompey." She was feeding the flames of Caesar's anger.

Shortly after ten, flanked by his Roman guards, Caesar conducted her to the throne room. Both she and Caesar were in white, flowing robes; her hand rested on his arm; his head was bent courteously toward her. They might have been father and daughter.

Before the great iron grillwork gate of the throne room they halted for the guard to announce:

"Julius Caesar, Consul of Rome, General of the Roman armies!"

In that second's pause she looked through the open spaces of the grillwork and saw her brother on the throne. He had grown older but his face was still that of a petulant small boy. At fourteen, what intelligence he had was undeveloped. Others had done his thinking for him.

Near him, talking to another councilor, was Pothinus. He was fatter. His costly robe could not disguise the corpulence of his body. His short legs could hardly sustain his unnatural weight, yet he stood arrogantly, master of the King and therefore master of Egypt.

The gates were thrown open. She walked in beside Caesar and heard the gasps and shouts from all sides. Ptolemy XII rose to his feet, pointing at her and screaming. Pothinus' face had gone a greenish white. His jaw had dropped so, in astonishment, that the fat jowls hung quiveringly down his neck.

From the throne came the screams: "Arrest her! Pothinus, arrest her! She's my prisoner—don't let her come here—"

His voice died away as Caesar approached him and looked at

him with stern admonition. With one hand Caesar guided Cleopatra to the steps below the throne; the other was upraised to still the noise. He faced the enormous room. He spoke quietly but he could be heard in every corner, by every person.

"Men of Egypt and King Ptolemy, hear me. Let my words be considered gravely, seriously, with sober consideration. This land has been torn by civil war. Your sons have died in battle; your households are divided in loyalty. This war must cease. It was my decision eleven years ago which reinstated Auletes, Ptolemy XI, on this throne. He was your lord and master and rightful king while he lived. His will and testament must prevail now that he is dead. To set aside that will, for any reason, would be to anger the gods and bring down their wrath upon your heads."

Pothinus cried: "This is not your affair, Caesar!"

One of the Roman guards took an angry step in his direction, but Caesar motioned him to stay.

"Do you question the right, Pothinus, of Rome to be arbiter of quarrels?" Such a tone in this man's voice was terrifying. It cut like a sword. "Did you question my right to interfere between Auletes and his faithless daughter, Berenice? Then say no more. Do not challenge me, or it will go hard with you."

Cleopatra's heart was beating rapidly. She had never been so impressed by any human being. This Caesar was steel where others were soft brass. He was greater; a leader beyond compare. He commanded obedience. Even her brother was momentarily speechless. Pothinus' face had turned purple-red with frustrated fury but he dared say nothing more.

"There is no legitimate reason," Caesar went on, speaking to the Alexandrian noblemen, "why this sister and brother cannot rule together. They must not be divided by the opinions or ambitions of others, if it be the will of their father that they occupy the throne together." He mounted another step and unrolled the scroll of Auletes' will and testament, and he read it aloud.

When he had finished he said: "Now you have heard. Do not

forget it again. It is the will of Auletes and it is the will of Rome that his daughter, Cleopatra, should be queen and that her brother, Ptolemy XII, should be king, jointly with her."

He offered his hand to Cleopatra and while the whole room held its breath, he led her to the throne beside her brother. Calmly, proudly, she seated herself.

A stir was seen in the crowd. Saat made his way forward and fell on his knees before Cleopatra. After a moment's hesitation, another man followed and did the same, then another and another. Movement in the crowd showed that others were ready to come and kneel when they were halted by a scream from the boy-king.

Ptolemy was in such a tantrum that he was tearing at his clothing. "I am king. Not she. Bend your knees only to me!"

And Pothinus played what was his trump card. "Caesar, she has broken our laws. She has defied religion. She refused to be the husband of her brother as she was supposed to do."

Cleopatra knew she must speak. Caesar could not answer this for her. She addressed them all: "Most noble lords of Egypt and my lord Caesar, I pray you to listen to me. It is true that the old law commands royal brothers and sisters to marry, if they are king and queen. But for the past years this law has been honored in form only, and not in fact. This is an enlightened age. I cannot be expected to do that which is abhorrent to nature. I have gone through the form of marriage to my brother; I have conformed to ritual; I can do no more."

Everyone looked at old Saat. He was renowned for his faithful upholding of tradition, religion and custom. Saat said: "There was a time, Queen Cleopatra, when I would have said you were wrong. Times change. It is wisdom to know when to change and you, who left us when you were only a girl, return to us a woman and there is wisdom and truth in you."

This was too much for the young Ptolemy. He jumped up, hurled his crown to the ground and stamped his foot. He tried to speak but he couldn't. In a paroxysm of rage he clawed at his face with his fingernails so that the blood ran down his cheeks. He ran from the room in tears.

Caesar was indifferent. He walked to the unoccupied throne and stood near it. "Now, may we discuss the matter of food for my soldiers?"

"Your soldiers are our guests. They shall be fed. I hereby name Saat as my chief adviser; he will see to the matter." And thus, swiftly and surely, Queen Cleopatra gathered the reins of government into her hands.

FIVE

MESSENGERS were sent to the army and to Achillas. The army was commanded to put aside their swords and come peacefully to their barracks. Achillas was ordered to report to the palace and yield himself to the clemency of the Queen.

The clemency was Caesar's idea. Cleopatra would have arrested him. "He plotted and he fought against me. He should be punished," she said indignantly.

"I am older than you," the Roman advised, "and I know there are times when you must punish and there are times to forgive. You need the support of all men of good will. Let them see you a merciful Queen."

So there were no punishments to anyone who had supported Pothinus or Achillas. Pothinus kept himself to the chambers of the King, sulking, but giving out reports that the boy was ill. He must stay there to look after his health.

"After that burst of rage, it would not surprise me if he were ill," said Caesar, "but I think he will recover. Let both of them sulk."

"I am not unhappy about it. It gives me time to do all the things I must." She must send word to the soldiers of her army in the desert, to tell them the war was over and that they could return to their homes. She must send them money and gifts and her gratitude. Besides the business meeting with her ministers, she must also give permission for the great celebration in Alexandria over her return.

She knew, with a feeling of happiness, that Caesar was beginning to admire and respect her more and more. It was a measure of how much he wanted to help her that he offered to give the island of Cyprus to Arsinoë as a little, independent kingdom. Having Arsinoë away would greatly ease the strain on Cleopatra, but Caesar would face criticism at home. Since when did Romans tamely hand back a conquered province to an Egyptian?

Trying hard to follow his advice, Cleopatra summoned Arsinoë and spoke to her kindly. "You have taken over my apartments while I was away. Keep them. I shall take others, temporarily, until you leave to rule your kingdom of Cyprus."

Eighteen months had not improved Arsinoë. Selfishness and spite had made lines in her pretty face. "Am I to be grateful for your castoff rooms? Am I to thank you for being banished to Cyprus?"

"Would you rather stay here, a younger sister without any prominence? Does Alexandria mean so much to you?" The Queen was astonished.

Hatred blazed out of Arsinoë's eyes. "If you had not come back, our brother would eventually have married me and I would have been queen, not you."

Cleopatra swallowed the words she wanted to speak. Her hand itched to slap Arsinoë, but the advice of Caesar had been to be merciful, so she was merciful.

He suggested, when Achillas arrived, that there be a great banquet of reconciliation. All of the leading figures of Alexandria were invited. Young Ptolemy came out of his sulking isolation and took his place next to Cleopatra at the table, with Pothinus and Achillas at his side.

It was the first time in over a year that she had seen General

Achillas, and she was puzzled at his politeness to her. It was out of character for the man, even if he had decided he must capitulate and be reconciled.

The banquet had been in progress for only a short time when she saw a man stop and whisper to Caesar. The Roman stiffened and sat up on his dining couch. His eyes went to Pothinus, then to Ptolemy and Achillas. He issued orders. The banquet hall was surrounded by his soldiers.

Two of them marched to the table and arrested Pothinus. In the instant all was confusion. People were screaming and jumping up from their places; Pothinus struggled. In the commotion Cleopatra missed both Achillas and her brother, and they escaped.

For once Caesar had made a mistake. Later he admitted it. "I misjudged the depths of hatred in your brother and Achillas, and the cunning of Pothinus. If I had not been warned by a spy, you and I would have been killed, Cleopatra. That was their plot. We were to be assassinated at the banquet. I have had Pothinus executed but your brother and Achillas managed to slip out of the palace and are now with their army. How large would their forces be?"

She could tell him. "Twenty thousand foot soldiers and two thousand cavalry."

"Against that I have only my few legions, your household guards and what recruits we can muster. My men are the best soldiers in the world; each one could account for five of Achillas'. But there is a greater danger." He led her to a window overlooking the harbor. "There is the fleet of ships which could mean our defeat. Every captain on them was picked by Achillas. They will do nothing—yet. But if we engage land troops and turn our backs to the harbor, they can land their sailors and soldiers and fall upon our rear. We would be caught in a pincer trap."

Caesar had done a great deal for her; now it was her turn to show him how intelligent and vigorous she was. "My knowledge is worth another thousand troops to us. I know where arms are stored in Alexandria. In the library are maps and charts which would be useful. I have spies who can slip through the lines and gather information. I will get word immediately to my men in the desert that they must not disband—the war is not over—and they must harry and ambush and ride against the rear guard of Achillas' army, as we used to. I can rouse the people against Achillas."

"Can you?" he asked thoughtfully. "Egyptian against Egyptian once more?"

"The desert chiefs did not call me Cleopatra—they called me 'Egypt'!" she answered, proudly.

In the first days of battle they were so outnumbered that they were slowly pressed back and back to the city gates of Alexandria. They made Achillas pay for every inch of soil he gained. Caesar was confident that he could win—if it were not for the threat of the fleet in the harbor.

She went with him into battle. He tried to keep her from the thick of the fighting, saying, "My soldiers are not used to the sight of a woman as a warrior. They become confused and think they must watch you and protect you, instead of watching the enemy."

So she stayed behind, but in plain sight so that the men of both armies could see her in her glittering silver armor and her bronze hair uncovered. She became a symbol to them all—either of courage or of dislike or of wonder. She heard that Achillas had offered a great sum of money to the man who would capture her.

Caesar's admiration was now boundless and genuine. He had never known a woman like her, he said.

"Egypt, women of courage are not rare. Intelligent women can be found. I have known beautiful women in every country. But to be all of these—brilliant, beautiful and brave—is a rare combination."

Appolodorus had gone back to round up the men who had fought with her in the desert. She knew that they were doing the best they could to hamper Achillas.

Slowly the tide began to turn for them. Caesar's soldiers had been in tougher spots than this one. They fought with disciplined valor for their beloved general. In the ten years of warfare since he had been a general he had taken by storm more than eight hundred cities, conquered some three hundred tribes and nations. His soldiers considered this rebellion of Achillas' with contempt. They were certain of victory.

A spy brought Cleopatra the information which Caesar most dreaded. Achillas had gathered together his best sailors and planned to slip them around the coast to board the fleet out in the harbor and then attack city and palace from the sea.

It could be done. Once the fleet was manned by experienced sailors and marines, they could attack the Lochias Promontory from the water and scale the palace walls with ladders or break down gates by heavy ramrod logs.

"We must burn those ships, Egypt," he said. "It is the only way."

She agreed. She could build other ships when peace came.

Caesar caught the captains of that fleet by surprise. Even so, it was a desperate battle before they were conquered and the ships set afire. Caesar and his men had to climb aboard from small boats. In the worst of the battle he was knocked into the water. Encumbered as he was with his heavy leather cuirass and the light iron breastplate and backpiece, he was almost drowned before he could pull himself to safety.

But, finally, the ships burned. It was an awful sight. From the palace windows the Queen watched as the blazing torches which had once been ships drifted rudderless in the harbor.

Suddenly she stiffened in terror. Five of the ships were being blown by the wind against the docks and warehouses. The docks were flaming within minutes; the warehouses with all their contents began to burn. She could see the tiny figures of men running to put out the flames with buckets of water. They were pointing at the museum. She looked, too, at the great white buildings. They were catching fire!

Her hands went to her face to hide the sight. She loved the museum and library. It was the pride of all Alexandria and the greatest of its kind in the world. She couldn't keep out the ugly crackling of flames and the groans and cries of other watchers; she had to look again. This time she broke down and wept.

Caesar found her there as he came in, triumphant, dirty and wet. His mood of triumph changed immediately when he saw that she was weeping uncontrollably. It was the first he had realized the tragedy of the museum. He was shocked because he respected learning, but he was even more horrified to find the strong and valiant Queen in tears.

He tried to comfort her. He soothed her as if she were a child. It was a strange experience for her. Mixed with her grief for the burning of the books, was this wonderful sensation of being protected and cared for by a man stronger and older than she.

As a leader of men, he was a heroic figure, but someone to be placed up on a pedestal. With his arms around her, cherishing her, speaking to her in kind and gentle tones, he became a human being to whom she felt closer than to anyone else.

She knew, too, instinctively, that his feelings for her were changing and deepening every day. He had loved many women, but he told her that none so amazed and interested and stimulated him as she.

At the moment there were more important things than love. She must dry her tears and let Caesar go back to his soldiers and the fighting.

During the night the wind veered and the city of Alexandria was saved. Demetrius and Josephus and the other scholars and many volunteers had labored to save most of the books. The others were lost: an irreplaceable treasure lost to mankind.

Also during the night Arsinoë and Ganymede slipped out of the palace, taking advantage of the turmoil of the burning. One of Arsinoë's maids, shrinking in terror, crouched at Cleopatra's feet and told her the story.

"I heard them talking when they thought I was asleep, Queen Cleopatra. Have pity on me—they would have killed me if I had tried to arise and warn you. The Princess Arsinoë said that now was the time to strike, that Caesar would be beaten by Achillas, but that the army of Achillas would be so weakened by the struggle that it would be easy to cut it to pieces from behind. The Princess and her tutor, Ganymede, took a great deal of money with them. They expect to bribe Achillas' soldiers, and their terms of peace with the King, Ptolemy XII, will be a marriage between the Princess and her brother. They go to Pelesium."

The woman was clinging to Cleopatra's feet. The Queen moved away, distastefully. "Get up. There is no need for you to be afraid." But she was furious at Arsinoë, more so than at her brother. Ptolemy was guilty of rebellion but Arsinoë was guilty of treachery. "Not only is she ungrateful to Caesar, but she is a traitor to me," she exclaimed to Charmian.

"She is also very stupid," said her attendant. "I know little of warfare, Cleopatra, but I am sure that Achillas cannot defeat Caesar."

She was right. Without the threat of the ships at his back, Caesar led his legions into a counterattack which pushed Achillas back. Street after street was reclaimed until they were out of the gates and into the open.

Here it could be expected that Achillas would have the advantage. Cleopatra watched as his dreaded chariots, with the knives set into the wheels, charged down on Caesar's foot soldiers. But the Romans had met chariots before. They knew just how long to stand and wait, until the plunging chariot and driver were almost upon them, and then just how to jump aside and thrust upward with their long iron lances to kill the drivers.

On the last day of battle the resistance crumbled so suddenly that even Caesar was startled. One moment he faced an army;

the next he saw only the backs of running, terror-stricken men. He soon learned the reason. By a freak of chance Achillas had been found by one of Arsinoë's hired assassins and stabbed to death. Without him there was no heart in the rebellion. Resistance crumbled fast.

They looked for Ptolemy and found he had died in battle. It surprised and gladdened Cleopatra to know that in his last days the youth had fought courageously. He had died better than he had lived.

Arsinoë was taken prisoner. Ganymede was executed. Cleopatra's younger sister was defiant and unrepentant. Caesar claimed her as his prisoner. Cleopatra was relieved to have that responsibility out of her hands.

At last the country of Egypt was at peace. The civil war had taken a toll in human lives and fortunes. Trade was at a standstill. New ships had to be purchased and business must be revived. The cities of Alexandria, Memphis and Thebes rejoiced with games and celebrations. The villages along the Nile welcomed back their soldier-sons, who were needed to till the fields and gather the grain. Barges began to move in safety down the Nile to Lake Mareotis, from whence their produce was carried through the city of Alexandria to the harbor.

The palace now held only two of Auletes' children: Cleopatra and her very young brother who was not even in his teens. To please the high priests she went through a scant form of marriage with him, but nobody took it seriously. Not only was he a boy while she was a woman of twenty-two, but he was sickly and dull-witted.

While the country rejoiced, Cleopatra had even more reason to be happy. She was in love. She had given her heart for the first time, and to a man whom she regarded with awe, respect and admiration.

Because of her unique position in Egypt as both queen and goddess, she did not consider herself bound by ordinary laws.

Openly and frankly, she declared Caesar to be her husband. She had chosen him. Caesar did not object to the name "husband." Egypt was far from Rome; what happened in Alexandria had nothing to do with his marriage to Calpurnia, in Rome.

As much as his cool and cautious nature would permit, he cared truly for Cleopatra. It was an unexpected thing to happen to him at his age: this ardent, openhearted devotion of such a beautiful and enchanting young woman.

He should have returned to Rome. With the defeat of Pompey, a great Day of Triumph awaited him at home. Honors and new titles would be his. Yet he delayed and delayed his departure.

Cleopatra couldn't bear to see him go. She had never known a father's love and Caesar filled that role. She had never been offered affection from a man she could wholly admire and look up to, and this experience opened all the generous warmth of her true nature. She became more lovely to look at and more enchanting to be with. At first Caesar was inclined to be amused at the way she flung herself with all her heart into this "marriage," but when he saw the depths and honesty of her emotion, he was no longer amused. He was touched by it.

But it would take more than emotion or her beauty to keep him in Egypt. She would have to be clever.

She possessed a talent, though she was only beginning to develop it. She had the ability to study people objectively. She could detach herself from them and from her own feelings and see them realistically. It was later to become a powerful weapon in her hands. She would, in the future, make mistakes about people but very rarely, and then only when their motives were beyond her understanding.

Now she studied Caesar and saw how she could hold him. She had penetrated the one tragedy in Caesar's life. Though he had married three times he had no son. If she could have a son of his, she would be truly his wife. He would raise her up above any other woman. Part of his wanting a son was his secret ambition. She had glimpsed an ambition in him which would have shocked republican Rome: he wanted to be king. A king was only half a king if he had no son to succeed and inherit that throne.

It would be many, many months, however, before she knew whether the child she carried would be a son or a daughter. In the meantime she must use her wits to keep Caesar with her. She saw that he briefly enjoyed the luxuries and the pleasures of the palace but that would mean only a little rest for him before duty took him away.

She had taken his measure. It would be the exercise of his mind which would keep him interested. So she invited the scholars and the best scientists to small parties.

Here Caesar met Sosigenes. The two men found an immediate, exciting interest in the new calendar which Sosigenes had been working on for years. "I must know more of this," Caesar exclaimed, as the three walked in the garden after dining. "Rome must have a new calendar. The one we have is unreliable and has become a political tool."

Sosigenes snorted. He was not in awe of anyone. "Your calendar, great Caesar, is ridiculous. Even our Egyptian one is better and I am working to improve it. Ours now has twelve months of thirty days each, with five extra days added each year and an extra one every four years. But yours! You work on a four-year cycle. Listen to this, Queen Cleopatra: the first year the Romans have four months of thirty-one days and seven of twenty-nine, and one month—"

"February, it is," said Caesar.

"Yes, yes, February—of twenty-eight days. In their second year, February has twenty-three days and they stick in an extra month of twenty-seven days." Sosigenes wagged his head in disgust. "The third year is like the first and the fourth like the second—except that the extra month is supposed to have twenty-four days! Can anyone make sense out of that?"

Cleopatra laughed but Caesar was in extreme earnest. "Something must be done. It is so serious that it is beginning to crack the very foundations of our country. Not even the priests know the exact date on which our religious festivals fall. The Senate or some unscrupulous politicians have even used the extra days and months to lengthen out their terms of office and played such havoc with dates that now the month of January falls when it is time to harvest instead of in winter."

He adjusted his long stride to the slower one of the scientist. "If I could bring back to Rome a new calendar, an honest and exact one, it would be more to me than all of the military triumphs I have had."

Sosigenes answered, "The calendar is not yet perfected. It will shortly be so, I hope, and it would give me the greatest pleasure, Caesar, to have your help and advice."

Cleopatra, listening to Saat with one ear while she overheard Caesar's conversation with the others, was pleased. This would be one hold to keep him here.

There were others. He was a shrewd organizer. She called upon him to advise her in these first troubled months of her reign. They were both plunged into the myriad problems of taxation, finance, the regulation of commerce, the reorganization of the Egyptian army, the conditions of agriculture in the Nile Valley.

"Your major concern," he told her, "is to get the grain out of the Nile Valley, where it has been rotting in warehouses, and down here to the coast, where it can be shipped out to buyers in other countries. Pay no attention to other demands if they interfere with this. I have heard it said that Egypt is the Nile and the Nile is Egypt; I never realized before how true that is. I'd like to see that fabulous valley and river sometime."

This last remark of his planted a seed in her mind. She had already seen, when the two rode through Alexandria, how keenly and with what great interest he observed everything new to him. He had been amazed at the great, wide thoroughfare of the Street of Canopus. "Our Roman streets are narrow tunnels, compared to this," he admitted. "I must make notes. When I am home I can, perhaps, rebuild and copy this."

On all sides of the street were colonnades and under them the shops of goldsmiths, silversmiths, jewelers and the dealers in medicinal herbs. The chariot-makers and wheelmakers occupied one whole section; further down were the craftsmen in leather and glass and copper and bronze and the shops that sold rare spices. On every corner were scribes in front of tables, who wrote the letters and documents which the untutored populace could not write for themselves.

The splendors of Alexandria, though, only reminded him of the city of Rome and his duty to return there. "I must see to the ships, Cleopatra, that will take my soldiers home. They must be provisioned and outfitted—"

"That work goes on," she assured him. "It is being attended to. You will suffer no hardships on your return to Rome. But tell me again about the terrible voyage you made to the island of Britain —I never tire of listening to it."

He had never had a better nor more charming audience for his tales. Most women were bored by accounts of warfare. Having fought in battles, she was honestly interested. He enjoyed talking; she liked to listen.

Three months went by. He began to speak more and more of Rome. Now she sprang her idea on him. "We will make a trip up the Nile, Caesar, to Upper Egypt which neither one of us has seen. I *must* go. The Ptolemies have behaved as if Egypt were only Alexandria. I know better. I want to see my whole kingdom. It is a fabulous country, where you will see the Great Pyramids and the Sphynx. It will be an adventure unlike any you have ever had."

He could not resist. The fabulous Nile Valley was a legend. He only hesitated to say, "I think you have bewitched me, Cleopatra. I should long ago have returned to my duties."

"We will only go up the Nile as far as you want to. We will only stay as long as you wish," she coaxed.

So one morning the large, graceful royal barge, painted red and gold, began its trip up the Nile. They traveled in style and comfort. Small boats constantly came and went, following them and bringing fresh fruits, the choicest of cooked meats, wines, flowers and everything they needed.

Over their couches on deck were silken canopies to keep out the blazing Egyptian sun. Slaves slowly brushed fans in front of them to keep the air fresh and cool. They were towed upstream through the flat, low, muddy lands of the delta into the running waters of the Nile. Here the oarsmen went to work.

Once in the swift-flowing river, Caesar could not be content lounging on the couch. He stood at the railing, fascinated. If he had not been a soldier and a politician, he would have been a great builder and administrator.

Through his eyes Cleopatra saw things she would have missed. She already knew, from her Council discussions, that the rise and fall of the river was regulated and that its flood waters were channeled off into reservoirs and canals, but it would not have occurred to her to personally investigate them.

Caesar often stopped the barge and insisted that they be rowed ashore. He questioned officials. He peered into canals. He climbed over waterwheels. He noted where repairs were needed; where a new canal or a road would be profitable. To keep up with him, Cleopatra was forced to walk through muddy fields, down the greasy wallows where the water buffalo had rolled. Her maids were scandalized. The poor, patient farm workers came crowding around, awed at actually seeing their queen.

"I expected to float up the river, not walk up the valley," she complained, when they were back once more on the barge.

"It won't hurt you," he answered. "As a member of a republic I'm used to visiting and talking to ordinary citizens. Do you think you are going to know your people by just sitting in that barge and looking at them as we drift by?"

So they stopped at every village. Petitioners came. The Queen was asked for a new grain warehouse, for permission to build a bridge, for redress of the wrongs committed against farm toilers by their overlord. Gradually, Cleopatra's interest was aroused. In the palace she heard generalities; here she was seeing the specific cases of need or injustice.

Never would she be republican in her thinking. From early childhood she had been imbued by tutors and by the high priests with the notion of her own divine ruling power. It was impossible for her to think that any lower-class Egyptian should voice even an opinion in government. But she was learning at first hand the problems of her government.

Caesar drew plans and blueprints. "Here there should be an aqueduct and there a canal. . . . A road should run from the last village to the warehouse. . . . You need more reservoirs to hold the run-off water from the Nile when it floods. I did not realize that it never rains here. All the moisture comes from the river. . . . The loading wharf here is a disgrace. The old, rotting timbers need replacing." On and on he planned the improvements for her. He was as eager as a boy.

At Giza they left the barge to visit the Pyramids and the Sphynx. Both of them were awed and speechless at these tombs and monuments of the Pharaohs, the ancient kings of Egypt.

At their next stop, at Heliopolis, they examined an obelisk. It was a tall, needle-like carved piece of stone that had been erected in Cleopatra's honor.

On they went, past Memphis, past Middle Egypt until they finally reached the lands of Upper Egypt. Here her tribesmen came to the river to greet her. She was proud to introduce them to Caesar, and she noticed his astonishment that she could speak their language and that they held her in such respect.

In fact, after a great day of celebration, when the desert chiefs gave a special exhibition of horsemanship and camel races, Caesar was so ignored by these men that he could stand it no longer. He demanded a horse, then ordered that his hands be tied behind his back. Sitting thus, with only his legs to hold him on, he spurred the horse into a wild gallop that brought forth cries of praise from the tribesmen.

Cleopatra smiled. He was much older than she but he could still act the part of an impetuous, young show-off.

At the town of Edfu they visited the temple of Horus that one of her own ancestors, Ptolemy III, had built. Caesar was interested in the construction of the temple, but she was emotionally and mystically impressed. Ptolemy III had been a good and strong ruler. Looking at the temple, she dedicated herself to carrying on his work. She would wipe out the stain of the weakened line which had brought forth such men as her father.

At the cataracts in the river, they turned back. They had been gone a long time and had seen much. It had drawn them still closer together.

As they drifted back for many days, they sat and talked.

"I want to rule wisely," she told him. "I have a sense now of the glory and greatness that used to belong to Egypt. The Pharaohs were leaders and strong men. Even the early Ptolemies were strong. For a woman to be strong and wise is not difficult, but for a woman to command and take leadership is not easy. Did you have to train yourself to be a leader, Caesar?"

He laughed and told her the story of how he had been captured by pirates when he was a young man. Up until that time he had shown no signs of being different from others. That marked a turning point in his life.

He had been with the pirates for thirty-eight days. "They were about to send a messenger to my family asking for twenty talents in ransom. That made me indignant. The amount was so small it dishonored my name. I insisted they ask for fifty talents."

Cleopatra looked at him and smiled. The code of honor among Romans was occasionally ridiculous. She said nothing.

"These pirates had to be impressed, by both me and my wealth and family. I was determined that I was not going to be treated as a prisoner. I watched them in their games. They were brutal. If they wrestled they tried to gouge out each other's eyes. If they fought with spear and shield, it was to kill. I was not as tall nor as large as some of them but I was in better condition. I challenged them all and beat them. From that moment on they deferred to me."

"Men may call you 'Queen,'" he went on, "but they will not follow or respect you until you prove yourself, Cleopatra."

"That may be true in Rome, where men are voted in or out of office. Here I reign supreme. I have the power of life or death," she objected to his statement.

"Nevertheless, they will rebel or they will criticize or work against you. Within a week I was no longer a prisoner of the pirates but their leader. I kept them on their toes. I showed them how to strengthen their small fort, and when they would not work, I lashed them with whips to make them. In the evenings I read poetry out loud to them or practiced making speeches. When they did not understand, I called them illiterates and boors. They did not dare rebel. I could think faster than they; act faster; outwit them."

"The gods must have been with you," she marveled. "I think no ordinary mortal could have done that, Caesar. I know you laugh at me when I say I share the divinity of the gods. I insist that you do, too."

"Perhaps." He did laugh but she knew he was pleased. He went back to his story. "That was my first taste of power. It was the first time I knew I had an ascendancy over other men. After my ransom was paid and I was freed, I immediately got ships and soldiers and went back to capture those same pirates. I had warned them I would. They had to be taught they could not touch a Roman."

A Roman, she thought. Always he mentioned "a Roman" as if other nationalities, even Egyptians, were something lesser. It bothered her sometimes, but when he looked at her she felt that his natural arrogance was becoming more and more submerged in his infatuation for her.

It was hard for her to find fault with him. She almost worshipped him. She wanted to know all about him but sometimes she almost hated his friends for owning a part of his life she did not share. He spoke so often of Marc Anthony. Anthony was younger. Caesar's fondness toward him was almost that of a father to a son, and Cleopatra was a little jealous.

Wait, she thought to herself, *until my son—his real son—is born!*

On the last days of the journey Caesar openly spoke to her of his dream of becoming king. She encouraged this dream, because she saw herself his queen. "It is not just for personal reasons that I will seek the crown," he told her, "but because I think it is the only way to heal the conflicts between the people and the Senate. In the old days of Rome, the ancestors of the aristocrats were valiant men, hard and tough, with a high code of honor. Now their descendants in the Senate have grown wealthy, soft and corrupt. On the other hand the free citizen can vote but he is so poor he is easy to bribe; he is uneducated, therefore he is easy to sway. Between the two—aristocrat and plebeian—there is a great gulf. Only a king can arbitrate between them."

When they reached Alexandria, Caesar put off his departure because the time had come for Cleopatra to give birth to their child.

In the autumn of 47 B.C., their child was born, a boy. He was named Ptolemaeus Caesar, but was called by everyone "Caesarion." Great was the joy of the father. By degrees, Caesar's feeling for Cleopatra had deepened; now he was ready to accept her even above his Roman wife, Calpurnia.

Solemnly and sincerely, he went through a real marriage ceremony in the temple, with Cleopatra.

As for the mother, she found herself caught in an emotion entirely strange to her, completely selfless, when she held her baby in her arms. "He looks like you. He is a little Caesar," she said to the man who was now officially her husband.

Caesar's hand touched the child's face tenderly. "I must go, first to Syria and then to Pontus in Africa. Rebellions have broken out in both places. When I am once again in Rome I will send for you. Trust me, Cleopatra. You are my wife. Caesarion is my son. Someday I shall be king and you will be queen, and we will reign over the world together."

SIX

CAESAR was gone. Though she loved him, Cleopatra's life was too full for loneliness. She had a country to rule and a son to care for.

Less than ten years ago she had been a puzzled girl, asking her teachers what *filial love* meant. She had been deprived of any real family affection. With the awakening of her emotions for Caesar and, especially, with the coming of her child, she was a changed person. She loved fiercely, passionately, devotedly. She spent hours bending over Caesarion's cradle, rejoicing in the perfection of the baby and making plans for his future.

Yet she was not privileged to be a wife and mother like any ordinary woman. Except in Egypt, Caesar was not recognized as her husband. Calpurnia had first claim on him. Nor could her dreams for Caesarion be untroubled ones. For his sake she must even doubt the word of his father.

She and Caesar might be separated for a long time. She was sure of his love for her but not of his political intentions. For the sake of Rome's supremacy in the world he might think that his relationship with an Egyptian—even a queen—would be harmful to his own country.

If he sent for her to come to Rome she would go, but she would only remain if he kept his word to make himself king and recognize her as his queen. She was as proud as he. Together, they could unite the world and leave it for their son to inherit.

Even without love, it would have been a fair bargain. Her name and family were older and had more prestige than his; hers was a royal family. Caesar would have that to add to the luster of his own fame. Could Calpurnia give him anything like that? From remarks which Caesar had made, Cleopatra knew Calpurnia to be an older woman, fond of her husband as he was of her, but with little fire or spirit to her.

It was not Calpurnia who worried Cleopatra. What might come between herself and Caesar was the jealous pride each one took in Rome or in Egypt. She and Saat had long talks about it.

"When I first saw that you loved Caesar," he said, stroking the beard that he was letting grow, now that he was becoming old, "I worried for fear it would turn your eyes towards Rome and loosen your ties with us. I feared that Rome would annex Egypt, through you."

"Never fear that," she assured him. "Though Caesar is my husband, the state of Rome is still an enemy to me."

He nodded his head. "I have come to believe—and so have the citizens of this country—that you, and only you, stand between us and the greed of the Romans. Use your influence with Caesar to keep us free! Even if you must give them Caesarion, make it part of the bargain that this country stays independent and that the Ptolemies, only, will rule it."

Under her guidance and the help of her ministers, the country emerged from the desolation of its civil war and began to regain its prosperity. Reforms were made; trade flourished; the harbor was full again with shipping.

So when nearly a year had passed and she received Caesar's invitation to come to Rome, she was able to leave Egypt in a prosperous condition. She looked forward to going, yet it hurt her to leave. Torn between these feelings, she boarded the ship which would take her away. As it moved past the Pharos Lighthouse the physical wrench of departure was so keen that she felt ill.

The parting words of Saat rang in her ears. "Take care, Queen Cleopatra! Trust not those Romans. Those who love Caesar may see in you a danger to him. Those who hate him will hate his son even more."

In a few days she was herself again. The baby turned out to be an excellent sailor, and this was a pleasant holiday for her, to be with him all day, with no other cares. Iras, Charmian and Appolodorus accompanied her. They were in high spirits. This was an exciting adventure for all of them.

Also on board the ship was her brother, Ptolemy XIII, the boy-king who was king in name only. He was a nonentity. He was too young and too dull of mind to be a danger to her, but she did not dare leave him home. Never could she forget Pothinus and Achillas. She would not have any one of her family left in the palace for ambitious men to use against her.

Most of the time she forgot he was around. She gave herself up to the excitement and anticipation of this adventure. She was going to see Rome! Her only thoughtful moments were when she reread Caesar's letters, trying to arm herself in advance with as much information as she could.

He went to Syria when he had left her, put down the rebellion there and returned for a brief time to Rome. This visit was made necessary because his good friend, Marc Anthony, had been acting the fool. Caesar had left Anthony in charge while he was in Egypt, but the young man had been extravagant and idle, offending many influential people.

Once that had been smoothed over and Anthony temporarily exiled, Caesar went to Africa to fight the rebellious forces of a man named Cato.

Who was this Marc Anthony? Cleopatra wondered. Would he

be back in Rome? Would he be for or against her? She wondered, too, if Caesar's long absences from Rome had been bad for his reputation or if his victories made up for his absences.

Her ship docked at Ostia, the port for Rome. She and her son and her attendants were carried by swift relays of litter-bearers into the city. The ship's cargo of her clothes and furnishings followed in carts. It was nightfall when they were brought to the first streets of Rome. She could see little except that they were narrow and crowded with small, brick or clay buildings. Once in a while she caught a glimpse of a larger edifice, white or gray, with round arched windows of stone.

Her litter was carried up a hill to a secluded villa. Servants greeted her. This was to be her home. There were many rooms, a gallery, a pavilion, a garden with a pool, but to her it seemed cramped and ugly after her great and beautiful palace.

She wandered about after Caesarion was put to bed; the others, weary from the trip, retired early. The night air seemed cold to her but it was the absence of Caesar which distressed her. Why was he not here? What did it mean?

This was an incredible way to treat a visiting queen. She had not been met at the ship's dock by senators or state dignitaries. She and her entourage had been brought to this villa almost furtively. She suspected the litter-bearers had instructions to come through back streets.

The more she thought of it the more furious she became. Of course, she could leave now and return to Alexandria, but everyone would laugh at her. She had to think. She had to be clever.

Caesar's affection for her might have cooled. He might only be wanting his son. Or, for matters of statesmanship, he might be embarrassed to flaunt his relationship with her. Obviously he did not at this time want the people of Rome to see the Queen of Egypt in all her royal robes and panoplies. She would have to be cautious, to find out what was in his mind and what the situation was in Rome.

Therefore, when Caesar did come the next day, he found her immersed in her role as Caesarion's mother. For the moment she was neither the charming girl nor the wild hoyden nor the regal queen; she was quietly and sedately the mother.

In flowing Grecian robes she met him, carrying the small boy in her arms. Caesar took a step toward her but she motioned him to stay back. Then she put their son down on the paved floor and let him toddle toward his father.

Caesar's manner was haughty, his expression distant and stern. Cleopatra held her breath as she watched him bend slightly to look at Caesarion. There was a startled expression on his face, and then he leaned forward and hungrily gathered his son up in his arms.

Not until then did Cleopatra move. Smiling, she came forward and put her hand on his arm. "Welcome, my lord Caesar, my husband."

He frowned. "I must ask you not to call me that here. Servants gossip. Two wives in Rome would constitute bigamy—"

"Look at your son." Now it was she who was distant and haughty. "Do you think anyone in Rome, servants or otherwise, can look at him and not know him for yours? Then what will you pretend I am—your mistress? Have you forgotten, Caesar, that I am a queen and not some pretty dancing girl? I will not lie or pretend. Under Egyptian law, you and I were married. You wanted to be my husband as much as I wanted to be your wife. Am I to hide here in Rome as if I were someone you were ashamed of?"

He sighed and sat down, still holding Caesarion. "Both your admirers and your enemies, Cleopatra, have spread all kinds of stories about you. Rome has talked of nothing else since the news of your ship's arrival. They say that you are beautiful only because you are an enchantress and a sorceress. They say you put a spell on me. They say you lived a wanton life before I knew you. They say you killed your young brother—"

"Enough!" She was outraged. "Let them be careful what they say. My brother is here in this house at this moment!"

Caesar went on, patiently trying to make her understand. "They say you fight like a man, think like a man, but use your woman's wiles to entice and blind men. They say you will be wearing barbaric and exotic clothes, and that the sight of you in your fabulous jewels will infuriate the poor people of the city."

She walked away from him, then turned and faced him. "My ship is still in the harbor. By tomorrow I shall be on board and on my way back to Alexandria, with Caesarion, unless it is understood that a queen is visiting Rome—a queen who is loved by, and married to, Caesar. A queen will be holding court here in this villa, demanding as much respect here as if she were in her own palace." She knew he would not care what people said of her, unless he feared it might damage his ambitions.

Their wills clashed. He was not accustomed to being challenged. He had expected her to be submissive and keep her presence quiet and discreet. In his anger he tightened his hold on the boy. Caesarion squirmed away and crawled to his mother, falling once but picking himself up without a whimper.

"Did I hurt the child? I did not mean to," Caesar asked anxiously.

"Yes, you hurt him. He is like me. When we are hurt we do not cry. But we will leave you—you have hurt us both." She started to turn away.

Caesar, mighty Caesar, was vanquished. "Stay. I have been wrong. I ask your pardon. The stories about you seemed to add so greatly to my burdens that I thought it best to keep your presence in Rome as quiet and as far removed from me as possible. I was wrong," he repeated, "because not only would I hurt you, whom I love, but I would have been a coward in the face of fire. It has never been my way to yield because of public opinion. I shall fight gossip just as I have fought other enemies."

He came to her, took her hand and led both her and Caesarion to a bench. "Sit here, and I will open my heart to you as I did before."

She forgave him. She smiled at him radiantly. Caesarion, too, though shy at first, rapidly showed he liked this new father and played happily with the buckles of Caesar's tunic while the other two talked.

"Poor little Queen," he caressed her hair, "I fear you will be snubbed and insulted. Not openly; they would not dare offend me that much. You will have to get used to being stared at, as a curiosity. But your talents will soon make this villa a splendid one. You will entertain. I promise to be here as often as I can."

She laughed as she looked up at him. "I am not afraid of insults. I can take care of myself, so long as I know that your plans for us are the same as they were in Alexandria."

"I am unchanged. My resolve has grown stronger. I must be king. But I must go carefully. Let Rome become accustomed to you. Let people know and respect your worth. I shall begin our plans by introducing an act into the Senate permitting certain Romans to have two wives," he said.

"Will the time be long? How slowly must you move?"

He frowned and said, thoughtfully, "The time will not be long, but I must make no reckless moves. I came back to find myself at the peak of popularity with the citizens. They will not stand in my way. But the Senate will be opposed—some senators, at least. The worst of it is that those senators are my best friends."

"Your friends? You joke." She stared at him in bewilderment.

"No. My best friends, except for Anthony who is as anxious for me to be king as I am. Brutus, who loves me as dearly as I love him, is the man I fear most. If he comes out publicly against me it will be extremely difficult. I must have him on my side, or keep him neutral."

"One man stands between you and a crown, and you hesitate to kill that man? How many men have you killed in battle to gain one mile of useless ground?" She was outraged.

Caesar leaned back and dropped his hand from her head. He put Caesarion down to play on the floor. There was strain and unhappiness in his face. Cleopatra, seeing it, clapped her hands for her slave and asked him to bring wine. When it was brought, Caesar sipped a little.

He answered her at last. "Perhaps you can never understand this, Cleopatra, because you are a foreigner and have not grown up in our traditions. Brutus represents the best of Roman virtues. In his person he upholds the pattern of morality and strength which was the pattern of our sturdier forefathers and which began the glory of Rome. There is no one like Brutus. He and I shared the same belief in discipline, the same love of freedom, the same strict code of behavior, the same honorable attitude towards the dignity of all Romans, be they rich or poor."

There was pain, even anguish, in his voice as he went on. "I am not now what Brutus is. I found I had to live in a practical world where one must make compromises. Yet I cannot sleep nights for wondering if I am ambitious only for myself, or do I act for the best of my country? Brutus is my conscience. I must make him see that this is not the Rome of our ancestors. It is different. If I am made king, and men must yield their freedoms to me, it is only so that I may preserve the rest: honor, courage, discipline and decency."

"If Brutus loves you, I should not think he would oppose you," she murmured. Much of what he said was incomprehensible to her. Republican freedom was foreign to her.

"He loves his code more than he loves any person . . . and where Brutus leads, Cassius and Cinna will follow. They are self-seeking. They were once my close friends but are now jealous of me. They will try to get Brutus to quarrel with me because if he becomes the leader of the opposition, then his reputation will give them a dignity they do not have."

"He will not quarrel with you, Caesar, over me. I will entertain him and his wife—he is married? Tell me what special dishes he likes to eat and what music is his favorite. Does he prefer the society of scholars or roisterers?"

"I cannot explain to you the kind of man Brutus is," he said, shaking his head. "The idea that I should be king will be repugnant to him, but a Caesar made king, with a foreign woman for wife and queen—this would be blasphemy to Brutus and he could call down the hatred of our gods upon me."

"Perhaps you misunderstand him. Perhaps he wants the crown for himself," she said.

"Never. Brutus is not loved by the crowd. He is respected, but not popular. He has too few weaknesses. He does not spend money for circuses or free bread and wine to treat the citizens."

"I do not think he will like me or that I will like him," she sounded so young and bewildered as she said it, that Caesar's look at her was fatherly and kind.

He said, "No, little Queen, I do not think you will like him, but you must try to charm him. It will be important." He rose to go. He was weary and careworn but in a far more gentle mood than when he had entered the villa.

"Must you go?" she asked.

"It is late and you are tired, and I have a great deal of work tomorrow." He stroked her soft cheek and her forehead. "I have been made Dictator for ten years. Now I must push forward plans and reforms so important, so sensational, that they will know I can rule with a firm hand."

After he had gone, the Queen put on a heavy robe and walked in her new garden. She could hear the constant and creaking sounds of drays and carts bringing merchandise into the city and taking refuse out. Roman law forbade them to use the crowded streets in the daytime. She wondered how anyone slept at night with this din forever in their ears.

The unknown Brutus loomed fearfully in her thoughts. She hated him for being an obstacle in her path. Surely Caesar must be wrong. No man could be so devoid of ordinary human weaknesses as he made Brutus out to be. It only remained for her to study him and find out what he wanted; where his pride or his ambitions led him.

She was a woman of many personalities. With so much gossip and slander against her, she decided it would be amusing to surprise them by being utterly different from what they expected her to be. She would stay quietly in her villa and see no one until the first of Caesar's three great Days of Triumph arrived. One Day was for Egypt, one for Syria, one for his victory in Africa.

In the meantime there was much she could do. She sent an urgent message to Sosigenes in Alexandria. She set about refurnishing the villa to suit her taste. Only Appolodorus went out to mingle at theatre and tavern with the Romans; he reported that the city was divided between curiosity over the Egyptian queen and the coming excitement of the three-day celebration of triumphs.

The first Day arrived. Seats were reserved for her and her party on the tribune, where she could watch the procession. She arrived late. The tribune was filled with all the world of fashion and wealth and senatorial rank; the streets were crowded with the citizens, when she was carried past them to her place.

Her appearance stunned everyone. Except for the gorgeous double crown of Egypt on her head, she was dressed in the utmost simplicity. Not one jewel or ornament marred the modesty of her Grecian robes. Not one touch of color disfigured their whiteness.

It was as if she said to all of Rome: *My beauty needs no jewels. My regal birth is served by this crown. My reputation can wear this spotless gown.*

Her unadorned loveliness made every other woman seem overdressed. Her youth and beauty and proud carriage provoked unwilling admiration. She paid no attention to the stares and whispers and the necks craned to look at her. She sat in her place, quietly and serenely.

She did not look at Caesar, sitting next to Calpurnia. Her indifference was noticed. Not until the trumpets blew for the start of the procession did her face show any animation or interest.

Since this day marked his exploits in Egypt, both she and Caesar had brought to Rome, in ships, all that was strange and wonderful from Egypt to show in this procession.

Now came the trumpeteers followed by Nubian noblemen in bright tunics. They carried falcons and hawks strapped to their wrists; they led lions and jackals and baboons by ropes of silver and gold. A hundred tribesmen on camels followed them.

Hippopotamuses were dragged along in cages. Elephants and other animals, captured above the cataracts in the far reaches of the Upper Nile, plodded or were driven or were displayed in cages for the awed and yelling citizens to see.

Next in the procession came displays of Egypt's agriculture and craftsmanship. Not only the citizens in the street, but the nobility in the stands leaned forward to judge critically the great sheaves of grain, the enormous glass bowls from the famous Alexandrian glass factories, the silver and golden platters, eight feet wide, which held fruits; the pottery and the figurines, the carved ivory, the alabaster jugs and the objects of hammered and enameled copper.

Then the religious part of the procession swept into view. Her high priests carried the sacred symbol of the scarab, or beetle, aloft. There were banners for the god Horus, represented by the disk as the sun. Other banners had the crossed arrows of Neith; the obelisk for Re. One priest wore a woman's gown and had on his head the cow's horns of the mother-goddess, Isis. An ibis head represented Thoth.

Then came the sacred bull of Apis, led by a priest. After that, for the more modern god of Serapis, a priest strode along wearing a fake beard gummed to his chin. The golden statues of Osiris and Isis finished that part of the procession.

The next part of this Day of Triumph belonged to Caesar alone. He left his place on the tribune and strode to where his chariot was waiting. At the signal, he got into it and, with uplifted arm, passed along the crowded streets to the screaming applause of all of Rome.

Cleopatra had expected something like this but she had not anticipated what would follow. She did not know that it was the Roman custom for a victorious general to bring back, as his prizes, the kings or queens or chiefs or members of royalty he had conquered.

In chains, half-walking and half-dragged, Arsinoë was the prize Caesar trailed behind him. Her linen dress was dirty and dusty from the streets. There were bloodstains on her sandals, from stumbling over sharp stones.

At that moment Cleopatra almost hated Caesar for being a Roman. She had no love for her sister. Arsinoë was a snake who would strike and strike, if ever she was free. But that a Ptolemy should be so disgraced, dragged in the dust behind a Roman chariot—that hurt Cleopatra's dignity and self-respect.

She closed her eyes against the sight and cursed the Romans under her breath, but she could not blot out the sounds of jeers as Arsinoë passed through the lines of people.

There was no use reproaching Caesar. He would not have understood. Arsinoë was more her sister's enemy that his; he had taken her prisoner; it was the Roman custom to exhibit royal prisoners—why, then, should Cleopatra object? So she swallowed the humiliation and kept her thoughts to herself.

The next day and the next saw more processions. Caesar was spending a fortune. He was making his bid for popularity by his generosity, and he was impressing his greatness upon everyone.

The stadiums were given over to free shows, sports and games. Hundreds of gladiators fought in the arenas for the public enjoyment. A mock naval battle was staged. His real soldiers became actors for one day and re-enacted some of Caesar's most notable victories, to the delight of thousands.

On the Day of Triumph for Africa, he made a speech, announcing that in that victory alone he had conquered for Rome a country large enough to give his homeland all the food they would need every year.

At the close of this gigantic three-day celebration he gave a great public banquet. Over 20,000 dining couches were set up. Food and wine were free to everyone. The whole city feasted at his expense.

When it was all over, he came to see Cleopatra. He was not a vain man—more self-confident than vain—but he welcomed her praises.

"After this how can anyone doubt that you are not like ordinary mortals?" she exclaimed. She was radiant. She had seen the most powerful nation bow down before its most powerful citizen, and she felt a secret triumph that it was she Caesar loved and would someday make his queen. "How could they deny you anything you want? You stood before them like a giant among children."

"It is going well," he agreed. "I was afraid that Marc Anthony's extravagances might have spoiled my reputation somewhat, since he was my deputy while I was in Egypt. But I find he was immensely popular with both the ex-soldiers and with the plebeians. It was only some members of the Senate whom he provoked, and they can do me no harm. Anthony is a splendid soldier and a gay companion, which made friends for him and for me."

He looked at her, keenly, and his face relaxed into a smile. "It may have been pure chance or it may have been your genius, but your manners and your dress these past three days have proved a masterstroke. The gossip still goes on about us, but with a difference. Your modesty confounded the scandal and your royal bearing commanded respect. I think it is time for you to entertain."

Every day for weeks she sent out invitations to the noble Roman families. They came, some impelled by curiosity and some from fear of angering Caesar. Only a few dared send their excuses, and among these was Brutus.

Those who came once, from curiosity or duty, returned again and again because Cleopatra fascinated them.

No one could say that she deliberately used her beauty to attract. Scandalous stories still were spread but without one word of foundation. She used her wit, her charm and her learning to entertain. She could discuss poetry with poets, drama with playwrights, music with musicians. She held old generals spellbound with her stories of desert warfare. She listened, gladly, to their boring accounts of their own campaigns.

With the wives she talked of her son and brought him out to be admired. The first time Caesarion was led into her banquet room by his nurse, everyone gasped. Caesar was there, and even though the boy was only a year and four months old, he was the exact image of his father. There was no question about it. One of the gossip stories had been that the Egyptian Queen was trying to foist off upon Caesar a son by an unknown father. Now everyone knew it was not true.

The one thing she would not discuss, except in the most limited way, was the politics of Rome. No one could inveigle her into making rash and damaging statements that could be used against Caesar.

Modest and young she looked, but they soon learned that she had a quick and sharp tongue and could defend herself.

Fulvia, wife of Marc Anthony, was a bold, rude woman who walked with a mannish stride. She said, "Tell us, Queen Cleopatra, do you remain with us long? I don't suppose there is much to occupy you back in your own country, since it is so small, but I should think you would miss all those good-looking

Greeks and Egyptians. I hear you are posing for a statue of your-self. Is it to be a gift to console us after you've gone?"

"Have you read Vergil?" asked Cleopatra sweetly. "Do you know his famous line: 'I fear the Greeks, even when bearing gifts'? I am Grecian, Lady Fulvia. Perhaps it would be better to fear my gifts than to wish for my absence."

That evening she raged to Caesar, "No matter what I do they will not like me. They come because they cannot stay away. I am the fashion. But not one of them is my friend."

"I tried to prepare you for this," he soothed her. "What difference does it make whether they like you, so long as they fear and respect you? However"—he paced the room with slow steps —"I will not conceal from you that I had hoped for more generosity toward you. Even Octavian resents you."

"Octavian!" she spoke bitterly. "That youngster, your grand-nephew, is one of the most disagreeable youths I have ever met. His smile is cold, tight and mean. His manners are unpleasant."

Caesar was angry at her. "Octavian is my favorite. I have adopted him. I will not have you speak of him thus. He is fond of Calpurnia and considers her unjustly treated. I cannot blame him for defending her. It is honorable in him."

For a moment Cleopatra was aghast. She had met—or, rather, had seen—Calpurnia, and had found her to be a woman of little personality, intelligence or charm. She was suddenly afraid. Did Octavian, and his family, mean so much to Caesar that he would waver in his loyalties and consider it more advantageous to keep Calpurnia and send Cleopatra away? But only two days ago he had introduced a law into the Senate permitting high officials, under certain circumstances, to have two wives.

Bewildered, she pulled her thoughts together. This was no time for her to give way to petty resentments and annoy Caesar. She smiled at him. "Forgive me. I shall not say anything against Octavian. I did not know you cared so much for him. Wait"—as he turned to go—"I have a surprise for you. I hope you will be pleased." She went to the door, opened it and motioned. Sosigenes' face appeared in the doorway, over her shoulder.

Instantly Caesar's anger was forgotten. "Sosigenes!" he exclaimed. "Welcome, my old friend. You have come just when I needed you. I have spoken about your calendar. I want to institute it if it is ready. Have you solved our problem?"

Sosigenes was equally happy to see Caesar. "I have come to the solution, but you may have difficulty just at first." Sosigenes undid a papyrus scroll and studied it as he spoke. The two men settled themselves on a couch. Caesar leaned eagerly forward. "In order to make the months fall in their proper season—you will have to add ninety days in one year—sixty-seven days between November and December and then twenty-three more at the end of February. That will start you off correctly. From then on, January must have thirty-one days, Sextilis and December must also have thirty-one. March, May, Quintilis and October already have that many. April, June, September and November must have thirty."

"But what of February? And how can the four-year cycle be adjusted?" Caesar asked.

"Give February twenty-eight days, but every fourth year add one extra day to it."

Caesar got up and paced. His face was alive. The careworn look had vanished. "I believe it will be successful. I must study it. If I propose it, Sosigenes, and it is accepted, it shall be called the Julian calendar, after my family name of Julian. But I shall give you the credit for devising it."

The two men settled into a long and complicated discussion of solar systems, dates and years. Cleopatra sat and watched them, thinking her own thoughts.

Hers was a difficult burden. She walked a perilous path. She must constantly win Caesar, over and over again, to keep him against all the pressures of his family, friends and political advisers. It brought her mind to its keenest and sharpest test. By bringing Sosigenes here she had succeeded—but what of the next time, and the next?

When he left that night, Caesar told her that he must leave in a few weeks for Spain and that he would be busy marshaling his soldiers and seeing to their outfitting. Pompey's sons were in Spain and they were stirring up trouble there; he must go to put down that rebellion.

She had the great and proud experience of seeing the Senate adopt the Julian calendar. More and more people flocked to her villa when it became known that it was her protégé, Sosigenes, who had devised that calendar with Caesar's help.

Even Brutus was interested.

SEVEN

ONE day, after Caesar had gone to Spain, she was talking to a good friend of his named Dolabella at a garden party in her villa, when she felt a stir go through the tree-shaded avenues and courtyard. All heads had turned toward the arched doorway leading from the house to the garden. The guests stopped talking or moving. A man and woman stood in the entrance, then came into the garden.

They were strangers to Cleopatra. She studied them as they advanced down the pathway to where she stood. The man was tall and handsome in a grave, distant way. He was younger than Caesar but his manner was not youthful. His wife, stately and attractive, walked by his side, and every now and then her hand touched his, as if by accident. It flashed through Cleopatra's mind that these two loved each other very much, in a world apart from others. The man bent once to ask something of his wife, and his face had a touch of gentleness in it then.

Why was everyone looking at them in such surprise? And what was the quality in their faces which was so different? Suddenly, she knew what it was. It was goodness. It was nothing kind or sweet; rather, it was a strong and noble sort of goodness. It flashed through her mind then who they were.

"My lord Brutus, my lady Portia," she greeted them as they approached. "I thank you for coming."

He bowed and Portia inclined her head slightly. "We trust, Queen Cleopatra, that you understand that duty and responsibility have kept us from paying our respects to your illustrious name and royal house, before this," he said.

That remark, she thought, could be taken two ways. Did he mean that his duty and responsibility to his state made it difficult for him to be respectful to a wanton Ptolemy?

She tried her best to win them both by the kind of flattery everyone else seemed to enjoy. "I am glad you could come today," she said. "I was not told your names when you entered but I knew you both. I have heard so much of Brutus and his lady, Portia, that I could not be mistaken. No one else could command such silent respect from all my guests. No one else could bear so easily the stamp of honorable distinction."

It was a mistake. The same faint expression of distaste crossed both their faces. Cleopatra saw it and understood: these two had no vanity and disliked gushing compliments.

She must try again. "Do not go," she put out her hand and detained Portia as she was about to turn away. Iras was approaching, with Caesarion taking tiny steps beside her. "I want to present my son." She sat down and Caesarion climbed into her lap.

Portia said gently, "He is a handsome lad." But in Brutus' voice there was a strange combination of sadness and stern judgment when he said, "Men make mistakes. It is a pity that children should suffer for those mistakes."

If anyone else had said that, Cleopatra would have lashed him with revengeful words. He had said, bluntly, that Caesarion was a "mistake" of Caesar's. He had said, all too plainly, that she was a bad mother, using her child to flaunt her relationship with Caesar. But she was powerless to say a word. Brutus' honesty had compelled him to speak. That honesty was his armor against anything she might have said.

They turned away. She sat, rigid and afraid. A voice behind her said, "Did you expect to make a friend of Brutus?" The voice was insolent. She raised her eyes to see a handsome giant of a man, with dark and laughing eyes, standing behind her bench.

He repeated, "Did you expect to make a friend of Brutus, Queen Cleopatra? Brutus has no friends. Either you admire and worship him or you hate him."

"Do you worship or hate?" she asked. She tried to pull herself together and be once more the charming hostess. Her smile was not a success.

"I? I am Marc Anthony. We have opposite natures, Brutus and I, therefore I do not love him. I worship only one man— Caesar—therefore I have no admiration left for Brutus."

Impetuously she cried to him, "If you are Caesar's friend, then you must be mine, too!"

"I am always," but his tone was light and guarded, "the friend of anyone so beautiful and talented as yourself, Queen Cleopatra. May I take leave for the moment? I see Dolabella approaching. He also is a friend of Caesar's, but none of mine. I do not like the man."

"Please," she put her had on his arm, "remain after the other guests have gone. I want to talk with you. You have been with Caesar in Spain?"

"Yes. He has forgiven me, recalled me from banishment, and we fought together in Spain as we have done so many times before." There was no doubting the genuine feeling he had for Caesar. "I shall be delighted to have a chance for private conversation with you later, Queen Cleopatra. Thank you."

He was gone, to mingle with the other guests. She saw Brutus and Portia talking with Sosigenes and knew that the scholar was the reason for their coming to her house.

Cassius, a lean man with a fierce and intense face, entered the garden. He had come often to her parties; he was one she instinctively distrusted. Today he seemed excited. He saw Brutus, and looked surprised. Then he made his way to him and began talking urgently and angrily. A small group formed around them.

She was curious. With Dolabella by her side she made her way as if by accident to where Cassius was. She head him say, ". . . is this to be called a conquest? He fights *boys*—Pompey's sons—who were only doing what any Roman sons would do in upholding their father's name. Yet he has sent word that his fight against them was a conquest, and he demands a Day of Triumph for it on his return. Once Caesar was modest. Now he sends messengers in advance to announce his so-called triumphs!"

Brutus gripped Cassius' arm. "Perhaps the messenger misquoted Caesar—"

"Or perhaps," Marc Anthony struck in hotly, "Cassius is so jealous of Caesar he begrudges him a triumph." His hand was on his sword at his waist.

Cassius, too, went for his sword but Brutus got between them. "Will you shame us all by fighting here, where you are guests? Will you brawl in the presence of Queen Cleopatra?"

He was protecting her prestige, while Anthony was outraging it, yet Cleopatra felt only resentment for Brutus and sympathy for Anthony.

She said, "I do not profess to understand all the customs of you Romans, but is it honorable in Cassius to defame Caesar, when Caesar is absent? I think if I were a man and a Roman, I would play the part of Marc Anthony."

Cassius managed to give her a stiff-necked bow. He turned on his heel and left the garden and the villa. Brutus looked questioningly at his wife; Portia nodded, murmured the polite and conventional phrases of farewell to the Queen, gathered her robes about her and followed Brutus out. The group of other guests around them broke up into twos and threes. Wine and cakes were served and the garden was once more filled with light and inconsequential chatter.

When they had all left, Anthony remained. He dined with the Queen. At first their conversation was of trivial matters: her impressions of Rome and his of Alexandria. It was when he was speaking of that city that she suddenly remembered him.

"I know you now!" she cried, interrupting what he was saying about the Street of Canopus. "You were the captain who came to Alexandria when my father was reinstated. I had forgotten your name."

"I had not forgotten yours," he said, gallantly. "I could never forget the little girl who was so angry when I criticized Egyptian royal marriage customs. You gave me a lecture on Egyptian and Grecian religion, in the loveliest voice I ever heard from a girl. If I had forgotten your name or your face, Cleopatra, I would always have remembered your voice."

She was pleased with him. She had been dubious because of his reputation as a wild, reckless spendthrift; as a man who liked wild, drunken orgies and had once driven his chariot through Rome, pulled by two tigers. There was the other side of him, though. He was reputed to be a magnificent soldier, a steadfast friend, the best orator in Rome. Now she discovered for herself that he was handsome and gay and likable.

Impulsively she said, "I hope you will like me for other reasons than my voice, Anthony. In spite of Brutus and his avowed feeling for Caesar, I think we two love Caesar the best."

He had great, broad shoulders and he shrugged them now, so that one strong, muscled arm was revealed. "I would die for him." He said it so simply that there was no question but he meant it. "I am not sure just where your interests would lead him. I am sure you mean him no harm, but do you understand his ambitions?"

She took a deep breath. If she misjudged Anthony, she might

be betraying Caesar's secrets. "If by that you mean his natural and rightful place as king—"

He started up from his dining couch in alarm. He placed his hand over hers, to silence her. "Hush. Speak softly. The day will soon come when all will call him that, but now we must only whisper it. Yes, that is what I do mean. If you are in his confidence then I am correct in thinking you also have your place in his ambitions. Having seen you, I think," he was nearly whispering, "that there could be no more suitable person than you to share his throne with him." He reached across and offered his hand. He smiled charmingly and boyishly. In his natural voice he asked, "Shall we be friends, then? Confide and take counsel in each other? My hand on it!"

She gave him hers. She felt buoyant, even gay. "It will be a pact between us. Now let us talk of other things. Tell me more of what you remember of Alexandria."

"I believe you are homesick," he said.

"I am. Everything here is strange to me. I am surrounded by people I do not understand, customs new to me, a city so crowded and noisy it seems ugly." She looked away and sighed. "There is no city so beautiful as Alexandria. I long for my palace instead of these cramped quarters. My people begin to wonder at my long absence from them."

"Poor little Queen." He took her hand again, but tenderly this time. "Who has been unkind to you?"

"Octavian dislikes me and I dislike him. That annoys Caesar," she confessed.

He raised one eyebrow in a comical way. "Why shouldn't he resent you? Or, rather, your son? Octavian has always thought he would be Caesar's heir when Caesar dies; he cannot relish the thought of a natural son taking the place of an adopted one." He rose to leave.

She walked to the door with him, her hand on his arm in a comradely fashion. "I did not know Octavian considered himself

Caesar's heir. That explains everything. Thank you, Anthony."

"And this day seals a pact between us." He lifted her hand from his arm and kissed it. Then he was gone.

Caesar returned from Spain in a determined mood. The time was ripe. He was convinced there would now be little opposition to his becoming king. He insisted upon another Day of Triumph so that he would feed and entertain the multitudes and thus keep his strong hold on them. He had new coins printed with his profile on them.

All through Rome his statues were crowned with laurel wreaths and crowns of flowers. More and more his name was said: *Divine Caesar,* instead of plain Caesar.

He bombarded the Senate with excellent plans which would mean employment for Romans. He demanded that work be started on the new port at Ostia; on a new theatre on the Tarpeian Rock; on new canals, bridges, and on the draining of the marshes. The calendar of Sosigenes was adopted and called the Julian calendar and was immediately popular.

He was elected Dictator for life. This honor made it seem positive to him that the next step to kingship would be easy.

Cleopatra was exultant. She dared wear some of her best jewels. Her house became richer and more luxurious. Caesarion rode with her when she was carried around the town; she wanted people to know and recognize him. Soon—soon all her dreams would come true, and she would be Empress of Rome as well as Queen of Egypt.

"It must happen soon," she spoke to Anthony when he visited her, alone, just before the Feast of Lupercal. "Have you noticed how many people now kneel to Caesar? Who would dare oppose him?"

"Cassius and Cinna will. I don't know about Brutus. He will probably register a protest and then retire from Rome and live his austere life someplace else. He is worried, I know. The words 'duty' and 'the republic' are constantly on his lips." But Anthony was happy and untroubled. "We shall catch them unawares. Plans have been made. I cannot tell you—not because I don't trust you, but because I want you to be surprised. People will be noticing your face. I can only say, wait until the Lupercal Games to-morrow, Cleopatra."

She coaxed him, but he refused. He laughed at her attempts to trap him. When he left, she felt better for his visit. Caesar had become so wrapped up in his ambitious dreams, so dedicated to them, that she could rarely even make him smile.

At the Feast of Lupercal, in the stadium the next day, she listened while the crowd cheered the winners of the events, but her eyes and her attention were all on Caesar.

Suddenly, after a laurel wreath had been awarded to one winner, Anthony appeared before Caesar. He held up another wreath, above Caesar's head, and he slowly turned and looked out over the vast crowd in the stands. It was as if he were silently asking the question: should Caesar take it?

Should Caesar have a crown?

For a moment the crowd semed puzzled. Then there was an outburst of yells and cries and cheers: "Take it, Caesar! Take the crown!"

Modestly, Caesar pushed it away. Again Anthony offered it. Again the crowd went wild with applause. Twice, three times Anthony proffered the crown to Caesar and three times Caesar pushed it away, but he did it with just enough hesitation to goad the crowd into louder and longer cries, urging him to accept.

To herself, Cleopatra applauded the plan. It was a good one. Whatever the next step would be, Caesar could now say that the crown was being forced upon him by the wishes of the people. He was not seeking it. Rome wanted him to be king.

"Hail, Divine Caesar!" the crowd was still shouting as the games ended, and they poured out of the exits. Moving with her attendants around her so that she would not be crushed, Cleopatra caught a glimpse of Brutus and Cassius. They were close together. The face of Brutus was a mask but he was listening to Cassius.

She saw Caesar the next evening.

"The matter," he said, "will surely be raised in the Senate. I can do nothing more. Fate has been set in motion and nothing can stop whatever will come." He was restless. He could not sit still. He was under an intolerable strain. All of her arts failed to keep him with her. Not even the sight of Caesarion or of Sosigenes could interest him. As he left he said, "You will understand that it is better for us both that I do not see you for a little while. At this crucial moment I want to be seen publicly with Calpurnia as much as possible." He kissed her and was gone.

One morning not long afterward, she awakened late. She had slept poorly. What aroused her had not been the usual soft singing of Iras or the prattle of Caesarion, but a frightful sound of screaming!

She sat up in bed. Outside her door—unheard-of sound!—was the wailing and crying of her slaves, her servants and her attendants. It seemed to her that the whole house was in an uproar. She called out: "What is it? How dare you make such a noise?"

The door opened. A slave burst in. He fell on his knees, bending his forehead to the floor, his face between his hands. His shoulders were shaking and a low moan escaped him.

"Tell me, what is it? Speak, or I will have you killed at my feet," she ordered.

"They have killed him! They have murdered Caesar. Wretched being that I am, to bring Queen Cleopatra such news! They have assassinated him in the Senate not ten minutes ago, and he lies dead at the foot of the statue of Pompey."

"Who has done this?" She could hardly speak. Her throat felt paralyzed by shock.

"The ones they call Cassius, Cinna and Brutus and many others."

She did not scream or weep or tear her hair. Caesar was dead! One moment she was gripped by intolerable grief for him; the next moment, it was forgotten in her fear for Caesarion.

If the assassins convinced the people that they had done the right thing in killing Caesar, because Caesar had changed from what he had been once, would they not seek revenge on those they blamed for the change? The stories had called her a sorceress and claimed she used witchcraft. It would be easy for an inflamed mob to blame her and her son as the instruments of Caesar's ambitious downfall.

"You may go," she commanded the slave. "Tell Appolodorus I wish to see him."

When Appolodorus came, sorrowfully, into her chambers she was dressed. Her mind was alert. She even noticed that there were signs of dissipation on him; he had evidently enjoyed to the full the pleasures of Rome. Could he once more rise to an emergency and help her?

"Caesar is dead, Appolodorus, and you wonder why I do not weep. This is not the time for tears. Take Caesarion, immediately, by the fastest horses and go to Ostia. There is an Egyptian ship in harbor—"

"The captain," he broke in, "is one Alystos. He was here yesterday to bring me news of my family."

She repeated as if he had not spoken, "Take Caesarion. Smuggle him on board that ship so that no one but the captain knows he is there. Hide yourself. Have the ship ready to receive me, but if I do not arrive by tomorrow night, you are to sail for Alexandria without me. I shall stay here to see if there is a chance to fight for his rights. He is Caesar's son and heir. If I can find his will—if I cannot, I will join you."

All that day she did not venture out. No visitors came to see her. Only her trusted servants went out, to mingle with the people in the streets and bring back the news.

She was told the people were in a somber, sorrowful but puzzled mood. They did not understand. Gradually, the word began to spread among them that the assassins were really the staunch defenders of Rome's freedom. They had acted in the best interests of the citizens. They had killed Caesar before he destroyed the republic.

By evening everyone was quoting Brutus. Brutus said he had acted out of justice, not from jealousy; from love and not from hate. He had killed the man who was his best friend, because freedom and the republic meant more.

A letter was smuggled in to her from Anthony. It said there were murmurs against her as the foreign seductress, but she was not to be afraid. He assured her in the letter that he would avenge Caesar and he would uphold the rights of Caesar's heir.

The funeral was the next day. Cleopatra left her house, heavily veiled, attended by Iras and Charmian, who were also wrapped up closely. The litter-bearers could only go part way, so dense was the crowd, and the three women made the rest of the journey on foot.

The atmosphere of the quiet streets, full of people who hardly spoke to each other, was frightening. All moved in one direction. On the steps of the Forum, Brutus would speak, then Anthony. Cleopatra arrived there and, by good fortune, was able to be close enough to hear, yet not so close she was in danger of suffocation from the tightly packed mob.

Her heavy, black veils went unnoticed. There were many veiled women. Besides, everyone's attention was full upon Brutus who had come out to speak.

He talked gravely, without fire or passion. He put forth reasonably and sincerely his motives for killing Caesar. He explained the dangers of a man like themselves, setting himself up above them to be king. His hands were dipped in blood but his heart was as sore as theirs. His motives were honorable.

The people listened. They nodded their heads sadly. Near Cleopatra stood a soldier in uniform and next to him a baker, judging from the flour imbedded in his hair and clothes. She heard the baker say: "It is true. Not even Caesar had the right to make himself king. I was carried away at the Lupercal Games; I would have given him anything."

Then Anthony stood before them. He walked slowly to the funeral bier and stood looking down at the draped figure of the dead Caesar. The throngs of citizens fell silent. Anthony's handsome, large figure seemed to carry something new to them— an emotion, a challenge. Then he spoke. His magnetic voice, so compelling that none could resist it, reached out to the farthest streets.

Yet at his first words Cleopatra was amazed. Was this a defense of Caesar? He was speaking in mild terms and acknowledging that the conspirators had slain Caesar for what, to them, were the best and most honorable of motives.

Then his voice changed. Sarcasm crept in. He repeated Brutus' words but with what a difference! Caesar was scheming to be king, Brutus had said. Of course he was. Had he not three times refused the crown in the sight of them all at the Lupercal Games?

Anthony's voice grew harder and more menacing. Brutus said Caesar deserved to die. Of course Caesar did. Had he not conquered the world and brought glory and riches to the people of Rome?

The crowd was stirring. Caesar's old soldiers were there. Under the sting of Anthony's words they were whipping themselves up to a rage on behalf of their beloved commander. Their grief was driving them crazy. Cleopatra saw the soldier next to her clenching and unclenching his fists.

It was correct—and Anthony's voice was bitter with sarcasm

—that Brutus should kill the man he said he loved. Did not everyone love Caesar? Did not Caesar love the people of Rome?

Cleopatra had not wept before but she did now. Everyone around her was weeping. She abandoned herself to an agony of grief. Through her mind crowded all the memories of Caesar: her first meeting with him, his help and guidance to her, their love for each other. He had been husband and father to her.

Never again would he ride a horse through her Egyptian deserts, with his hands tied behind his back. He would fight no more battles. He would never be king. She would never again see him lift Caesarion in his arms.

Now that he had reminded the crowd of the Caesar whom they had loved, Anthony did not bother with sarcasm. With his audience whipped up to a frenzy of grief and rage, he named the conspirators, even Brutus, as plain assassins. Then he held up Caesar's last will and testament.

Cleopatra stiffened. Her tears stopped. Now it was coming, the revelation to all of Rome that Caesarion was his son and would be his heir. She made ready to throw off her veil and reveal herself. This crowd would love anyone whom Caesar had loved. They would regard her son as heir not only to estates, but to his position as future consul—perhaps future king.

She heard a great yell. She turned to Charmian. "What did Anthony say?"

"Caesar has left money to be distributed among the people. His city lands will become parks for their enjoyment. We must go, Cleopatra," Charmian whispered. "These people are so emotional they are out of control. They want to kill those who killed Caesar, but they are in a state to kill anyone."

"But he has not finished reading the will! I cannot go until—"

Then she heard Anthony's voice again. She heard what he said but she could not believe it was true. Octavian was named as Caesar's heir. Not Caesarion, but Octavian.

"That is the old will," she said, frantically resisting Charmian's attempts to pull her away. "Has Anthony played me false?"

"Please come," Iras begged. All around them the crowd was shouting, milling around, peering into faces, tearing aside veils and cloaks, seeking anyone who might have been in the conspiracy to kill Caesar. Finally Cleopatra let herself be pulled along by her attendants. They were fortunate in being able to slip away unnoticed.

Hours later, at home, she was still incredulous. "I do not believe it," she repeated over and over. When Anthony arrived she flew at him. "Why did you read that Octavian was the heir?"

"Because that was the will. I do not like it any more than you, Queen Cleopatra, but it is the truth. I have searched everywhere for another will but none exists. If I could only find some proof, some writing in Caesar's hand, that he officially named Caesarion, then I would be appointed his guardian and would look after his interests. I cannot do it now."

Cleopatra paced up and down. She was so bitter she could not even pronounce the name of Caesar. "He acknowledged Caesarion publicly. Is that not enough?"

"It gives you a claim. But it also brings a danger. Octavian will not forget that claim. He may try to get rid of the boy," Anthony warned. "I cannot protect you in Rome. Brutus and the others have fled from the city but they will return to fight. If they just run away and hide they will be admitting that what they did was wrong. I know them. I must act immediately to set up a government here; get troops together and prepare for the battle which will surely come. Because of this will, no government can be formed without Octavian in it."

He was already in his officer's uniform. He could stay only a few moments. He was impatient to be gone.

"Wait, Anthony. Only tell me this—why? Why did not Caesar act to protect his son? No father ever loved as dearly as he loved Caesarion," she said.

He looked uncomfortable. "I do not know. Perhaps he meant to but there was not time since he returned from Spain. Perhaps he thought it best to wait until after he was crowned. Perhaps he felt he needed Octavian's help until then."

Anthony left and she was desolate. All of his excuses seemed reasonable. Any one of them might be true, but there was another reason which Anthony would be too gallant to mention.

Caesarion was half Ptolemy. He was not pure Roman. Caesar may have realized that if he died, an Egyptian mother would be his son's guide and teacher. A foreign influence and foreign blood would enter the highest place in Rome. Caesar had loved her and he had loved Caesarion, but Rome was more important to him than any single person.

Out of desolation and grief grew her bitter, bitter anger. Never again would she trust a Roman, she vowed.

"Quick," she commanded. "Strip this house of everything I brought to it. Take my jewels and precious articles that are small enough to carry. Burn the rest. I will leave nothing here for these barbarians to gloat over. We must be in Ostia before that ship sails."

On the voyage home she was like a woman out of her mind. She seethed with hatred, was wild with despair. She would sit motionless for hours in apathy, then this mood would be followed by one of such pointless energy that she paced up and down the decks furiously. At such times Iras and Charmian dreaded her stinging hand and bitter tongue.

Everything she had fought for was gone. All her splendid dreams had ended with a dead man at the foot of the statue of Pompey. She had trusted and loved, and now she was hurt and disillusioned. Her love for Caesar had been the finest thing in her life, but in the end he had rejected her and her son and played her false.

What was awaiting her at home? She had thought to come

back to Alexandria as the Queen of Rome and Egypt, bearing her people the greatest of gifts—the guarantee of their sovereign independence as a nation. But what now?

On that voyage her brother, the boy-king, died one night. His body was buried at sea in the early morning before anyone but Cleopatra, Appolodorus and the captain knew what had happened.

The word was given out that Ptolemy XIII had died of illness, aggravated by the voyage. But was it true? Iras and Charmian avoided looking at their Queen; they did not dare. In her present temper and furious anguish of mind, she was capable of anything. All that mattered to her in the whole world, now, was Caesarion—and Egypt. The young Ptolemy *had* been ill. The rough voyage might have brought on his death. Her maids could only wonder and suspect; they knew that Cleopatra wanted him out of the way. As long as he lived he had been a threat to her and an obstruction to Caesarion's becoming king some day.

She could be ruthless for Caesarion's sake. As the ship made its way homeward, slowly the scar tissue formed over her wounded spirit and she could think and plan once more. She centered her thoughts on her son.

He would not suffer. She made up her mind to that. He belonged only to her, and she to him. She would raise him to be a fine man and a strong ruler. She would return to Egypt and put all her strength into building up that country for her son; when she died she would leave him a country rich, powerful and free of Rome.

Her homecoming was a strange one. It disturbed her. She was cheered as she stepped onto the docks. People gathered to look at her. But the cheering was small and subdued, and the faces of the Alexandrians were guarded in their welcome of her.

The first person she gave audience to was Saat. "From you, my old and trusted friend, I want the truth. How am I regarded in Alexandria? What has been said about my absence?"

"Opinion is divided," he said. "Those of us who know your wisdom have counseled patience. We have said that you went to Rome to help Egypt. We have said that Caesarion would be honored equally by Romans and Egyptians. That would ensure our country's independence. The faultfinders have spread the word that you would not return. We would be ruled from Rome. You neglected us. Everything that has gone wrong, from a sandstorm blighting the crops to the failure of a waterwheel, has been laid upon you as your fault."

She had not listened to Caesar for nothing. From him she had learned when to strike, when to compromise, when to be silent— and when to speak out.

"Saat, call an assembly of the Alexandrian nobles, the high officials and the politicians. Even the high priests must come," she ordered. "Bring the generals of the army and the captains of my ships. I will talk to them."

He left her and she sought Caesarion, and the two of them wandered through the palace. The boy did not remember it. He was amazed at its splendor, while she wondered how she could have been content, for one minute, away from it. Its beauty soothed her. Its magnificence restored her identity and her confidence.

They came to the square, high windows and she exclaimed at the soft, cool breeze, "How I have missed this!" Warmed by the sun and cooled by the sea air, the climate of Alexandria was almost perfect. She felt as if she could breathe again.

"The Egyptian sun has put new color into your face already," marveled Iras. She and Charmian were like children, they were so happy. They had been afraid of Cleopatra on the ship, but now they saw that she was beginning to walk with a light step again and smile more often, so they laughed and sang all day long. Appolodorus vanished for two days to visit his family.

"None of us realized how homesick we were," Cleopatra answered Iras. "Rome was an alien land. We were not ourselves there."

The love she had had for Caesar had burned to ashes. Dreams of world empire were gone. In their place had come an even more intense and fervent love for Egypt. Her dreams and ambitions were solely for her own country and people.

At the great assembly she ordered the doors thrown open so that all could see and hear. Even for so huge a room as this audience chamber there were too many people. They overflowed into halls and anterooms. She sat on her throne, receiving their kneeling homage. She searched every face for signs of what they were thinking.

When all had gathered she stood up and addressed them.

"I have been away from you too long." Quietly her beautiful voice reached them, in intimate friendliness. "It has been a burden upon me to leave my country and dwell among strangers. I have been often sad and always lonely. We Egyptians do not transplant easily. I had to leave you, from necessity."

Into the sweetness of her voice came a challenge. "Do you question that necessity? Do you ever forget that Rome has only to land a few legions here to enslave us? I have seen how lustful they are for conquest. They do not live, as you do, to enjoy life. They live to conquer. I, and I alone, have kept you free. Caesar might easily have made Egypt a province of Rome. Because of me, he did not do this. Because of me, he even handed Cyprus back to Egypt.

"Because Caesar is dead," she lashed at them, "you will say I have failed. Our protector is gone. Because Caesarion is not acknowledged his heir, you will say my time was wasted in Rome. You will feel disgrace because the father thought fit to slight his son. Am I to be held to blame because monsters slew Caesar before he could take steps to uphold Caesarion's claim?"

She stood before them, magnificent. She knew that she had surprised them by speaking so frankly and by scolding them as if they were her children. "You are wondering about the future. Perhaps some of you think that this is the time, while Rome is torn by quarrels, to build up an army and deny the usual tribute to Rome. If that is what you want, very well. I will lead your army. When Roman legions come here I will march out to defend us. But, remember!—out of your pockets will come the money for that army."

Pausing for a moment to let them think of it, she caught Saat's eye. He was approving her and nodding his head, to show how he felt. She continued: "Your sons, who have lived for their pleasures and their studies, will be the officers of that army. Many will die. They will be opposed by Roman veterans. Trade will come to an end. If that is what you want, say so now; I will not oppose you."

As the ringing words died out there was silence and then the embarrassed shuffling of feet. Eyes were lowered. Faces turned away.

When she spoke again, it was in a quiet and reassuring way. "Think well. This is not the time to annoy Rome by denying the small tribute. We are free. Our ships sail unmolested. No armies trample our crops. Your homes and your sons are safe.

"I do not promise you," she moved a step forward, "that my reign will be free of trouble. I cannot predict what will happen but this you must know—"

She stopped and waited until it seemed as if everyone held his breath for her next words. Small as she was, she held them in the palm of her hand, by the strength of her voice and her mind.

She cried out: "This you must know, that I stand between you and disaster! So long as I live, Egypt shall be free!"

EIGHT

HER speech dissipated completely whatever mists of suspicion or distrust there had been in the minds of the Alexandrians. They knew she spoke the truth. They looked up to her superior intelligence. They were content, from then on, to leave their fate in her hands.

Cleopatra was not too proud to take advice. The day after the assembly, she spoke privately to her few trusted councilors. To them she could say things she could not say openly, where some spy might have reported her words to Rome.

"There is only one way to withstand Rome," she began the discussion. "We must outwit them. We must be more clever than Octavian, bolder than Anthony, more subtle than Cassius, and always regard Brutus as our enemy, no matter what happens. There will be civil war between those men. On which side shall Egypt be?"

Old Saat was surprised. He raised his wrinkled eyelids and peered up at her. "I thought that Anthony was your friend. I thought he would revenge the murderers of Caesar."

"No Roman is my friend!" She was angry. "We will pretend friendship, if necessary, to use them. But to which side? For a while they will not think of Egypt, until one side or the other needs more of our grain or gold or ships. We must judge, at the right moment, which one will likely win, and we must step in with our offer of support."

"And if the winner is Brutus?" asked one of her councilors.

She bit her lip. A shadow passed over her face, making it less than lovely. How could she admit, to herself as well as to them, that she hated Brutus not only for the killing of Caesar? He was the only man who had been able to make her despise herself for her cleverness. Compared with his nobleness of mind, she could not be sure of her own. "If Brutus wins," the words stuck in her throat but she forced them out, "then we must pretend friendship but be ever on guard. He hates me, but there is one thing in our favor—if he gives his word to protect Egypt, he will keep it."

They agreed. Saat would then have spoken of local problems, of the rebuilding of ports and fortifying defenses, but he was interrupted. The captain of the household guards had a question to ask of the Queen. He put it bluntly:

"Queen Cleopatra, everyone is asking what happened to your young brother, the King?"

"He died on the passage homeward." It was all she would say. She looked at them and dared them to ask more questions.

For more than two years, from 44 B.C. until the end of the year 42 B.C., the titanic civil war raged in Rome between the forces of Anthony and Brutus, and prosperity reigned in Egypt. Merchants and traders grew fat in wealth. The Nile Valley was developed further, with new canals and new irrigation systems, new warehouses, roads and dams. Grain from Egypt went to all parts of the world. Egyptian ships and Egyptian sailors were considered among the best.

Cleopatra kept in constant touch with what was happening, although winter storms might delay a messenger for weeks. She heard that Anthony and Octavian were forced into an alliance. A man named Lepidus was included to make it a ruling triumvirate. An army had been gathered by them to fight the one which was growing under the banners of Brutus and Cassius.

Sooner or later a decisive battle would be waged between those forces. She would have to make a decision so that whoever won would have to acknowledge her as a helpful ally.

During this time of peace she could give aid to her special project—the rebuilding of the university of Alexandria. She began ambitious designs for the library and museum. It would cost a tremendous fortune to make them as they were before, but she repaired what she could. The scholars flocked back to the city.

There were some days when she put aside business and allowed herself to indulge in the luxurious idleness which the Alexandrians expected of her. She had revolted against the simple and modest clothes she had worn for Caesar, and now she wore the rich, exotic garments, the ornaments and perfumes she loved.

Her beauty ripened. When she entered a room, when she walked among her guests at a party or sat with them at a banquet, the unusual magnetic quality of her face drew attention away from women who were even more beautiful. Many princes and kings of small, petty countries sought her hand in marriage. Handsome, distinguished Egyptians and Grecians pursued her.

But she had grown cynical about them. Appolodorus worried for her. On the occasion of his marriage to a nice, pretty girl of good social standing, the palace celebrated his wedding and he took that opportunity to speak his mind to Cleopatra.

They were such old friends that he dared to say what even Iras and Charmian hesitated to put into words. As the guest of honor for the evening his chair was beside the Queen's, with his bride on her other hand. The banquet room was gay with laughter and witty talk, with toasts to his happiness, when he leaned over to say, "And when will you marry again, Cleopatra? Surely you will not live out the rest of your life a lonely widow?"

She gave him a teasing, mocking smile. "You desert me. You

feel guilt. Now you would see me consoled? What husband will you choose for me?"

"The prince from Cilicia?" he suggested.

"Too ugly. I cannot abide a man with such a long nose and weak chin," she answered.

"The son of Herod Antipater?"

She shuddered. "Doubtless he will be king of Judaea if Anthony triumphs. The two are friends. But I do not trust him. He has been educated in Rome and I fear he is more crafty a Roman now than even a Cassius. An alliance with Judaea would not be a bad move, if I could control a Herod. I fear not." Still smiling, she asked, "Why should I marry? Why are you insistent?"

"Because," he said boldly, "the reputation you had before, for wantonness, was false. Now you amuse yourself. When one favorite bores you, you take another. I fear that reputation is becoming true."

With one quick, heedless motion she picked up her glass of wine and threw it into his face.

The talk and laughter around them was instantly stilled. The little bride cried out in fright. Appolodorus sat without moving, not even wiping away the wine drops on his face. Cleopatra took a deep breath and then said, to all: "You misunderstand. It was an accident. I was laughing and about to offer a toast; I turned and upset the wine glass."

When the talk had resumed she said in a low voice to Appolodorus, "Forgive me. Long ago you earned the right to speak your mind to me without fear. I was angry, partly because you spoke the truth and partly because I envy you for your happiness. I do want marriage. I am by nature a faithful and constant woman. But after being Caesar's wife, what other man could satisfy me? What you call wantonness is a searching for someone with only a spark of his brilliance, an iota of his strength. I meet someone and I think he has a little of Caesar in him, only to be disappointed again."

Appolodorus had wiped his face with a napkin. Now he put it down and asked, "Do you not hate Caesar?"

"I try to. I want to. I hate the Roman pride he could not put aside, even for me. But in the dark of night I remember that he loved me, taught me, helped me, and I am a woman crying for the man she worshipped and a child crying for her father."

He put his hand over hers. It was all he could offer her to show he understood her loneliness. She shut her eyes against the tears. Her hardness and cynicism were a shell. Underneath it she still had the capacity to love.

As soon as Appolodorus, his bride and the guests left, she went to the room where Caesarion slept. She bent over his bed and his sleeping form and gently touched his forehead with a soothing finger. The boy smiled in his sleep. Unconsciously he knew that gentle touch.

In her face, now, was all the tenderness and sweetness that Appolodorus could have wished for her. Toward Caesarion she was never anything but good.

She had spoken the truth when she had said to Appolodorus that by nature she was a faithful and constant woman. She would have been happy with a husband and a large family. Circumstances forced her out of her natural role, so all the maternal love centered upon Caesarion and all her devotion on her country.

The boy was growing. At four he was sturdy; at five, he was tall for his age. The mother's eyes would have been blind to faults but the queen's eyes searched him for weaknesses. Rejoicing, she could find none. Caesarion's mind was quick to learn. He already knew his alphabet and was beginning regular studies with tutors.

He took bumps and falls without whimpering. He was obedient to his teachers, respectful toward older people, never mean to those who served him. Yet he had an independent turn of mind.

If there was one single thing she could complain of, it was that he seemed more Caesar's than hers. He had all his father's good qualities, but he lacked her fluid responsiveness and the changeable moods which so well expressed the stimulation of her spirit. Most of the time he was a happy, but grave, little boy.

She learned that Anthony had forced a bill through the Roman Senate, making Caesarion the legitimate son of Caesar.

This surprised her. Did Anthony still remember her? Did he still feel friendly toward her? No, she decided. "He does not do this because of any fondness for me," she told Saat. "He does it to have a weapon against Octavian. I predict that that alliance between them will not last, even if they defeat Brutus. Octavian will resent Anthony's popularity. Anthony will want a legitimate reason—such as Caesarion's claim to be Caesar's heir—to use against Octavian someday."

Saat reluctantly agreed. "You know these Romans better than I do, Queen Cleopatra. Still, I shall spread the word about Caesarion throughout all of Egypt. It will add to the pride your people have in you and enforce their allegiance to your son. We must thank Anthony for that much."

More news came from Rome. Octavian had married. His bride was Fulvia's daughter by her first husband. She was not Anthony's child, but the alliance tied the two men together. It was a completely political marriage, since the girl was only *eight* years old.

Angrily, Cleopatra remembered that Fulvia had sneered at the marriage ceremony between Caesar and the Queen of Egypt— yet she was capable of forcing her child to go through a wedding ceremony simply to unite the families of Octavian and Anthony.

The civil war was gaining momentum. The final clash was near. Daily, hourly, Cleopatra watched and waited and listened to reports. In her mind the scales slowly tipped in Anthony's favor.

She had liked him, but that would not have weighed in her decision. Friendship meant nothing. She would have thrown her aid to the side of anyone if it would help Egypt. What came to weigh most heavily in her judgment was the bold, daring, aggressive character of Anthony and the fact that he had with him all of Caesar's veteran soldiers. Brutus was strong, she thought, but not strong enough for that combination.

It was almost disastrous for her, then, that the first demand should come from Cassius. If he had been in Rome she could have ignored it, but he was in Syria and close enough to march overland if she refused. He wanted money, ships and men.

Her advisers were fearful. She played a delaying, compromising game. She wrote answers to Cassius which were so ambiguous he could not think she meant to refuse, yet which would not harm her if her letters fell into other hands.

She waited until the same request came from Dolabella. This was not much better, but it would get her out of an awkward position. Dolabella and Anthony disliked each other for personal reasons, yet they were fighting on the same side. She immediately sent ships and twelve thousand soldiers to him.

Three days later Saat came to her, wringing his old hands and wearing a long, despondent face. "The ships and men were captured! Cassius took them, claiming they were the ones you had promised him. It is whispered that one of your captains was a traitor and steered the fleet to where he knew Cassius was waiting."

To Saat's great surprise, she threw back her head and laughed. "I did not plan this—I am not that clever!—but our gods are watching over us, Saat. Now, whoever wins, I can avow that I tried to help him. If Dolabella and Anthony win, then my ships and men were meant to go to them. If Cassius and Brutus triumph, I can say those same ships and men were the gifts I promised Cassius. But I must do one thing more. Send two more ships along the same way, to search for any of the fleet that might have escaped Cassius. It will be fruitless but I will have proved good faith, if I must ever need explain this to Anthony."

She saw Saat's eyes fixed on her face, with a strange expression in them. "Well?" she asked, impatiently.

"The Queen of Egypt," he replied, slowly, searching for words, "cannot be compared to ordinary mortals. You must be more shrewd, more ruthless, than we. Your mind must go into paths we cannot follow. But I have known and loved the Queen for many years, and I am sad for her. The girl I once rolled into a rug was too simple and direct to be devious."

"Our enemies, Saat," softly, she answered him, "are more devious, more crafty than I. I must fight them, in every way I can, for our freedom."

He was growing too old to kneel. He bowed, instead. "I know. Forgive me for any hint of criticism. You must do what you must. I may not like it but I will support it."

The year of 42 B.C. was drawing to its close. Rain was falling upon Alexandria when, one day from her window, she saw a ship coming into harbor. She was puzzled because it was a Greek merchant vessel but it held so little cargo that it rode high out of the water. "Send that captain to me as soon as he comes on shore," she commanded.

When he came, the captain was dripping wet from the rain. He apologized for that and for his unshaven, unkempt appearance.

"I come from Greece, from a town called Philippi, and I set sail from there in such a hurry—I was so anxious to get away after the battle—I wasn't sure but that they would take my ship—"

She cut him short. "What battle? Who were the warriors?"

"The battle at Philippi, Queen Cleopatra, between the great Roman generals. It is the end of the civil war. The battle was a terrible one, a war between giants—" he said, but she interrupted to cry out at him:

"Who won? Tell me who won!"

"The forces of Marc Anthony were triumphant, gracious Queen."

It came as a shock to her how much she had wanted Anthony to be the winner. "Bring a dry cloak for this captain," she ordered a servant, "and a hot drink. Now, continue; tell me everything you know of the battle. Was Octavian there?"

The captain made a gesture of contempt. "Oh, yes, he was there—hiding in some reeds, the coward. Anthony faced Cassius. On his flank, Octavian faced Brutus. While Anthony was winning and pressing hard against Cassius, Octavian was being driven back by Brutus. So much so that he ran away and hid in the reeds. Luckily, Anthony saw what was happening and galloped his horse over to the fleeing army of Octavian and rallied those men to come back and fight."

With the dry cloak around his shoulders and the hot wine in his hands, the captain was more comfortable. "You understand, Queen Cleopatra, that this information was brought to the port and to me by men who actually saw what happened. They say that, just as Anthony had his weak comrade, in Octavian, so did Brutus lose the battle because of Cassius. Driven back by Anthony, Cassius lost all hope. He was out of touch with Brutus. He believed it was total defeat so he fell upon his own sword and killed himself."

"So Caesar is avenged by the death of one of his assassins!" exclaimed the Queen.

"Aye—not only of one, but of two. Brutus was so beset by the entire army—Anthony's men and Octavian's, whom Anthony had rallied—that surrender was inevitable. Brutus would not do it. He had a servant hold his sword and then he ran himself upon it." He shrugged his shoulders. "They are strange people, these Romans, to do things like that."

"They died by their own hand." Once the Queen would have thought this strange, but she had come to accept this code as her own. It was as important to die with dignity as to live with it. "And Anthony is the hero of the day at Philippi?"

The captain waxed eloquent. "He was a giant of a man and as brave as his stature and his heart. They say he went joyfully into battle and that he was in the thick of it. His great size made him a target for every spear and arrow, but no wounds could stop him. Reckless and daring as he was, his men would follow him anywhere."

The memory of Anthony came vividly to her mind and she smiled. She would like to hate all Romans, yet she found herself exulting that he had won.

She gave the signal that the audience was over. The captain was leaving, when she called him back. "What happened to Octavian? Did Anthony kill him, as he should?"

"The boy who hid in the reeds? I do not know. I did not hear. My ship was ready to sail," was all he could tell her.

Certain that he had told her everything he knew of the battle, she dismissed him with the present of the borrowed cloak and a small bag of gold coins.

For a month afterward the palace was amazed at the restless, overwrought feverishness of the usually poised Queen. Cleopatra would not be still. Questions and hopes possessed her; she paced the gardens, even when it was raining, and walked through the magnificent rooms without seeing them.

Anthony had won. Her whole future and that of Egypt's turned on his victory. He could be friend to her or she might find he had dismissed her from his thoughts. Like all the others, he would probably want gold from Egypt but, unlike the others, he might be willing to grant favors.

Anthony was not as ambitious as Caesar. He liked the role of king-maker better than that of king. Might he not be willing to push Caesarion forward? Might he not be persuaded to be as ambitious for the son as he had been for the father? Now that Octavian was dead—for surely Anthony would kill such a coward!—there was no other heir to Caesar's lineage, honors and estates but Caesarion.

At the end of the month word came. Octavian lived. Anthony had, contemptuously, sent him back to Rome. But he had let him live.

Never had her attendants seen the Queen in such a rage. She picked up a priceless porcelain vase and smashed it on the floor. She threw her hand-mirror against a wall and shattered the glass to bits. No one dared speak to her unless she spoke first. She would talk only to Saat. He shared her concern, if not her anger.

"This fool! This stupid, stupid Anthony," she said to Saat. "He had every reason to kill Octavian, as any general can decree death to a deserter. Now he has let Octavian free to scheme and plot and raise himself up to be another Caesar. Doesn't Anthony know that he and Octavian are too different to rule together? Doesn't he realize that Octavian will hate him because Anthony was a hero while he was a coward? Let them quarrel! About that I do not care; but I do care that Octavian stands in Caesarion's light!"

"Do not fret yourself with what cannot be helped," he advised. "We have worse problems to consider. Since their victory, Anthony, Octavian and Lepidus have consolidated their Triumvirate. In an informal manner they have divided up their spheres of influence. Anthony has taken as his portion all of the East—Greece, Syria, Phrygia—since he plans to begin the campaign against Persia next year."

"And without question, he will be wanting gold from me. He will probably demand the reasons why Cassius got the ships and men, instead of Dolabella." Cleopatra sighed. "You are right, Saat. This is no time for the luxury of anger."

She sent a carefully worded letter of congratulations to Anthony. She reminded him, in a delicate way, that they had been united in their love for Caesar.

Not long afterward she was strolling around the hill of the

Temple of Pan. Caesarion, now six years old, was with her, and she pointed out to him the half-finished buildings of the museum and told him stories of when she had once studied in that vast building.

"Did you study well, Mother?" he asked.

"Very well. Sometimes, at first, I was willful but my teachers were as stern with me as if I were not a princess. Demetrius would frown; Josephus would shake his head; Sosigenes would scold me."

The boy was aghast. "Scold *you*, Mother?"

Behind them a voice spoke. "I agree with your son, Queen Cleopatra. I cannot imagine anyone ever daring to be harsh with so beautiful a child as you must have been."

She turned. The man standing there was a stranger to her; Roman by his tongue; a Roman of some importance, by his rich tunic. She was affronted. She said, "Sir, do you not know that when I walk here with the young Prince, it is forbidden for others to wander through these temple gardens?"

He inclined his head in a bow. "So I was told, but my errand was so urgent I dared to come. I am Dellius, the envoy of Marc Anthony. My message to you is so urgent, I hoped you would forgive my taking this liberty."

"If it is so urgent," her heart was beating rapidly, "then we will return to the palace immediately. I will call together my advisers to hear you."

He put out his hand to stop her as she started to move away. He had an intelligent face, but there was mischief in it. "May I suggest that we speak here, alone, first? Until I saw you and watched you I had no thought but to discharge my errand in the proper way—a formal meeting, to which I would bring the demands of Anthony to the Queen of Egypt."

"Demands?" she asked.

"Marc Anthony is angry over that matter of the troops you sent to Cassius—"

She protested, "I sent them to Dolabella. Cassius intercepted them."

"I do not dispute with you, Queen Cleopatra, but Anthony will." He shrugged his shoulders. "Words and explanations will not move him. Arguments will bore him. Let me help you with good advice."

"Why should you want to help me?" she asked. She saw Caesarion's tutor, waiting discreetly at the foot of the small hill. She gave the boy a gentle push and sent him to join the tutor. "Why," she asked Dellius again, "should you want to help me?"

He paced the gardens beside her. "I am Anthony's envoy and would do nothing against his interests. But I am also an admirer of the unusual, the exotic and the beautiful. I believe I will do Anthony no greater service than by smoothing away all problems that might stand between you two, because I think the sight of you would give him more pleasure than the sight of your gold."

Though she kept her thoughts to herself, she was measuring this man, Dellius. He was a familiar type to her. He was not a great man in himself, so he enjoyed meddling in the lives of the great. It would give him satisfaction to think he was manipulating the plans of Anthony and Cleopatra. Let him think so. He might even give good advice, since he had so obviously become a victim of her charms. "Tell me what to do, Dellius." She was demure. "I shall be guided by you."

"Anthony is in Tarsus. It is a port of Cilicia, in Asia Minor. He is resting his armies and preparing for the campaign to conquer Persia. Go there, Queen! Sending letters and reasonable arguments or gold or tribute—these are poor substitutes for the presence of yourself. Anthony is now enjoying himself; he is in the mood for good company, especially that of a beautiful woman."

"I do not think his wife, Fulvia, would welcome me." She pretended to object, though her mind had been made up, swiftly, to go to Tarsus. "She never approved of me."

"Fulvia is in Rome. She is behaving badly. Power and ambition have gone to her head, and she fancies herself a strategist who will outwit Octavian to further her own and Anthony's interests. She is stupid. At this moment Anthony wants no problems with Octavian. Yet Fulvia does everything she can to cause trouble between them. She had Cicero killed, because he was Brutus' friend. Cicero was one man she should not have touched; his reputation is above all feuds. When Octavian returned to Rome his legions wanted the land they had been promised. He agreed. Fulvia objected. So Octavian was able to say to the soldiers that he was willing they should have land—only Anthony and Fulvia opposed the rightful claims."

"It is always a mistake for a woman to match wits with men." Her eyes never looked so bewitching as when secret laughter glinted from them. Dellius saw only the bewitchment and missed the laughter.

During the four days before he left for Tarsus, she flattered him by pretending to take all his advice—while, in private, she made her own plans. *Go demurely,* he counseled. *Throw yourself on his mercy; Anthony cannot resist the tears and entreaties of such a woman as yourself,* he told her.

And she said, *Yes, Dellius,* while at the same time firmly resolving there would be no tears, no begging and no entreaties.

Soon after he left to tell Anthony she was coming, her preparations were ready. Twelve ships were filled with household and personal treasures. Great chests of silks and linens; chests of jewels and precious ornaments; chests for her gowns, her cosmetics, her perfumes filled the holds of three ships. Even such a fleet as this could barely accommodate all her attendants, all the musicians, the acrobats, the magicians, poets, dancers, actors she took with her.

And the ships themselves were dazzling on the blue Mediterranean. They were painted in vermilion and green, coated with gold, outfitted in the costliest woods with the oars dipped in silver. The sails were of purple silk.

The finest cooks of her palace went with her. One ship was a veritable garden of small trees, shrubs and flowers, tended by gardeners who were artists in their work.

When she sailed, she left Caesarion behind. She was fighting for him and for Egypt. She meant to charm Anthony and the maternal role would bore him.

When this fleet arrived, finally, in the small river of Cydnus and then sailed into the lake that made the port for Tarsus, it caused enormous excitement in that town. She could see the crowds lining the docks; more and more people running from the center of the town to see what was happening. She ordered her captains to drop anchor. No one was to go ashore. Rowboats came from the docks to ask what fleet this was and then scurried back with the information that the Queen of Egypt awaited the coming of Marc Anthony.

She waited. She would not humble herself by going ashore to seek him out.

Soon, at the dockside, she saw a tall, handsome figure in an officer's informal tunic, surrounded by other Roman officers. He was an arrogant figure, so much larger than those clustering around him. He stared at her ships, bent his head slightly to listen to what someone was saying. Then he got into a boat and was rowed toward her.

She had won this first opening move! She had forced him to visit her.

When Anthony swung himself on board he stared around him as if he could not believe what he saw. In the center of the deck a great couch served as a throne for Cleopatra; it was covered with gold cloth and she, too, was dressed in gold. Beside her stood Iras and Charmian. Overhead a silken canopy was embroidered with the crown of Egypt.

Slaves conducted him to her. For a moment they regarded each other, unsmiling. He neither bowed nor spoke.

"My lord Anthony," she said at last, "my very good friend, I have traveled far just to thank you for avenging the brutal murder of the man I loved." So might a queen thank one who has done her a service. It was as if she were under no obligation in coming to Tarsus except to please herself.

"Queen Cleopatra," he said her name, wonderingly, "have you grown more beautiful or was I blind when I saw you last in Rome?" He seemed too caught up in his own emotions to speak of Caesar or that avenging. "All of Tarsus is saying that the goddess Aphrodite has sailed into this harbor today. I believe they speak truly. I think you must be Aphrodite come back to a mortal life."

"I am mortal enough to be flattered by such words from you," she answered. Now she was smiling. "Since we last met you have become the greatest of heroes. All the world speaks Anthony's name with respect. When I heard of the battle at Philippi I feared that you might have received some injury, but you appear to me younger and stronger than ever before."

Anthony could not keep from staring at her. "I lived through that battle and others, without a wound. Have I come to the time when I will be vanquished, not by a sword, but by a woman's smile?"

His words could have been mere gallantry, but a shock ran through her. His eyes were serious. And she—who had sworn never again to trust or care for any Roman—was shocked that those words could bring her so much pleasure.

NINE

THAT night and for three nights following, the Queen of Egypt entertained Anthony and his senior officers at banquets. Each evening was a fresh surprise.

For the first banquet her cooks provided a dinner of unusual and delicious foods. Three of her ships were moored close by and musicians on board all three played and sang in turn, so that it seemed to the bewildered Romans that music floated to them through the air from every direction. This first evening the Queen behaved with great formality; with all the protocol of royal etiquette.

Anthony was impressed. His manner was as correct as her own.

On the second night she unbent enough to laugh and tease some of the younger officers. She was gracious with them, but she looked up occasionally to smile at Anthony as she would to an intimate friend.

Anthony had a natural love of gaiety. He responded to her own, and he was delighted at the entertainment for that evening, when acrobatic dancers performed in the very rigging and on the masts of the ship.

A scene of barbaric splendor awaited them on the third night. A great silken tent had been erected on the deck; her slaves and attendants were dressed in the costumes of desert tribespeople. It was an imitation of her adventure on the desert, except that the campfire glowed in a great silver brazier; the dining couches were covered in leopard skin; the armrests were saddles, but those saddles were of silver, softened by Persian tapestries. The imitation stars overhead were made of precious jewels.

During the banquet a poet recited legends, stories and poems of the desert. Afterward, the only entertainer was the Queen, herself, who took the lyre and sang songs she had learned sitting around a real desert campfire.

When Anthony took his leave, his eyes were dancing with teasing laughter. "Ho, Egypt!" he exclaimed. "I think you are being *too* clever. I was going to ask a modest sum as penance for your having let your ships drift away to Cassius instead of Dolabella. But after such a display of wealth as you have given us, I shall ask for much more money." He ran down the gangway, still laughing, and into his own boat.

For a second she was taken aback. Then she ran to the railing and called down: "Ho, Roman! You are the host in this country. Is it not the custom for a host to give gifts, not ask for them?" And she waited for that wonderful laugh of Anthony's to come rolling back over the water to her.

On the fourth night her guests walked the length of the ship on a carpet of fragrant roses. Everywhere bloomed the loveliest of flowers and shrubs. Her throne was a bower of exotic blooms.

This time Anthony lingered long after the others left. "So you think now to pay me with flowers?" he asked.

"I shall not pay you at all," she answered. Joyful lights glinted and shone in her eyes. Her mouth was mocking.

"What!" He pretended to stagger and fall down on the thick piles of rose leaves. "Am I to get nothing? Am I to forget all about Cassius? And the ships and gold and men he got to help him, from Egypt?"

"Yes. From secret Egyptian lore I will teach you to forget.

Let me see—there is a powerful drink which causes forgetfulness. No, that will not do. There is dust from the tombs of the Pharaohs. If I were to sprinkle that on your eyes you would remember nothing. But then you would forget me, too."

He reached up a hand to her. "I do not want to forget Cleopatra. But you must give me something if I am to forgive you for Cassius. What of a kiss?"

"You would exchange a kiss from me for the fortune in gold? You are gallant, Anthony." She leaned down to kiss him at the very moment he pulled at her hand; she lost her balance and fell beside him into the softness of the flowers.

It was good to laugh. It was so long since she had romped and teased and kissed someone with such a light heart!

"Cleopatra," he said when they sat up and brushed petals out of their hair, "I think you have cast a spell over me. I did not find you so beautiful and desirable in Rome. Perhaps," he spoke soberly, "it was because you belonged to Caesar and we both thought only of him."

It was so wonderful to be gay that she didn't want to remember Caesar. She said, "Do you really think me beautiful? You are mistaken. I put a potion in your wine. You cannot see that I am actually ugly and old and hideous."

"So you are!" He leaped to his feet and, with one easy, strong gesture, lifted her up to face him. He peered at her. He threw back his head and roared with laughter. "So you are!" he said. "Strange that I never noted how ill-favored you are. What does a man do with such an ugly woman? Reason with her, argue with her, beat her?"

"Neither, my lord." She backed demurely away from him. "One leaves her. So you must leave me and I must say farewell."

"Only until tomorrow. Prepare another potion and I shall think you beautiful again." He kissed her hand.

She stood at the ship's railing looking after the boat that took him to Tarsus. It was dark. The approach to the port was by a small river which then widened into this beautiful lake harbor. Flickering torches, both from the decks and from ships, threw yellow lights on the ripples of the water. Now and then she could hear the barking of dogs from the town; fainter noises might be from music in taverns.

She was disturbed. She could not be falling in love with Marc Anthony! Her plan had been to charm him into making advantageous agreements between Egypt and Rome. She had meant to take advantage of his gallant reputation and do it coldly and ruthlessly.

Even while she despised herself for softness, she could not help remembering how he looked, how he talked, how he towered, so tall and broad-shouldered, above other men. She could not help but contrast his gay disposition with Caesar's grave one. He was much younger than Caesar. And she? She was only twenty-eight. Was she to deny herself forever the right to the sweetness and the joy of love?

What was Anthony's history? She knew he came from a distinguished family. As a young man he had been sent to Athens to study. He learned just enough so that he could not be considered poorly educated; in fact he distinguished himself in oratory. Then he became bored. He was wild, reckless, fond of amusements, eager for danger and adventure. He dropped his studies to join Gabinius as a young captain and came with him to Alexandria at the reinstatement of her father.

But it was in Gaul, later, that his bravery came to the attention of Caesar. The older man took a liking to him, pushed his promotions. Anthony developed a fanatic loyalty to Caesar. When civil war broke out between Pompey and Caesar, Anthony had the courage to stand in the Senate against the bill which would have taken soldiers away from Caesar, then he fled, disguised, to join his beloved general in Gaul.

Caesar trusted his loyalty but not his reckless behavior. In battle, Anthony was cool, daring and a superb leader. In peacetime he drank too much, liked pretty women too much, and spent his tremendous energy on wild escapades.

Fulvia ruled his household. He did not care, so long as she left him free to enjoy himself.

Could she possibly love such a man? Cleopatra wondered. All of caution she had learned from her experiences with people warned her against him. All that was lively and quick and temperamental in her responded to the lively spirit of Anthony.

In her anguish of conflict, she struck her hand against the railing so hard that she tore the flesh. Blood seeped from it. Charmian came hurrying over with a cloth for a bandage.

"You have hurt yourself! You are bleeding, Cleopatra!"

"It is nothing, nothing. I am angry at myself so I hurt myself. Charmian, we must leave here. The Romans are my enemies. I cannot—I will not love another Roman. I hate them."

Charmian was skillfully binding her hand, while Iras stood by, watching sympathetically.

"May I speak a word, Cleopatra? You will not be angry?" asked Iras.

"Speak." The Queen was still sobbing.

"I think I have never seen you so happy with any man. Your face is alive with mischief and happiness. Even when you are just thinking of him there is a smile on your lips. I mean no disrespect to Caesar, but I wish you had met Anthony first. He has the same youth, fire and spirit which you have."

"Do you care nothing, Iras, that he is a Roman? Have you forgotten how one betrayed me?"

Iras hung her head but she said stubbornly, "Anthony would never betray you. Even—even if he had to leave you, he would always keep you in his heart. Besides, I think your nature, Cleopatra, is stronger in many ways than his. He could pick you up by one of his big hands and break you in two, but you could rule him."

Cleopatra listened and wanted to believe. Her reason said that it was madness to allow herself to fall in love. But if she were the stronger? Then perhaps this love might be permitted to her, and still not be disastrous to her country.

In the morning she was again fearful. She had changed her mind. When Anthony came she told him, "Today we must discuss the serious matters between Egypt and Rome, if it so suits your convenience. I must leave for Alexandria quickly."

"You cannot go. I will keep you prisoner here," he said, dismayed.

"Prisoners are unhappy. They languish and die. They learn to hate their captors."

He exclaimed impetuously: "Then I shall follow you to Alexandria!"

She was so pleased she could not but show it. "Why should you not come to Egypt? Winter will be here before you are ready for the Persian campaign and you cannot move then. Why spend all those months in this small and dreary place when you can be in Alexandria?" In her own city she would be the ruler, and he would be the visitor.

"I will come," he promised. He saw the bandage on her hand, and he examined it with fingers incredibly gentle for so big a man. "How did you do this? Was some slave clumsy?"

His touch broke down every defense. "I did it," she said, in a small, low, gentle voice, "because I wanted to punish myself for caring for you. I do not want to be fond of you. Contrary to what gossip says, I do not love lightly."

Unconsciously, he gripped her wounded hand tightly but she paid no heed to the pain. "Until this moment," he said, "gossip spoke truly of me. I have loved lightly, but my feeling for you is deep."

In the days to come the hardness and cynicism which had grown around her like a shell dissolved. Never had she been so happy. If Anthony lacked the grave purpose she had admired in

Caesar, he had qualities of humor and cheerfulness and gay animal spirits which made her feel like a very young girl.

In turn, she constantly amazed and surprised him. They had spent the last afternoon, before she must leave, fishing from the side of an old, deserted dock. They had dirtied their fine clothes, got their feet wet; their hands smelled of fish; her hair had come unbound and hung in a coppery cloud around her shoulders. She had been a laughing and carefree hoyden, and he thought the role suited her.

But when he asked, "What shall I give you as a farewell gift? It will be weeks before I see you in Alexandria," she instantly became serious and answered:

"You know that the glory of Alexandria was our famous library. It burnt when Caesar fired the ships. I can rebuild but I cannot replace the books—unless you are willing to make me a great gift. Near here, in Pergamum, is a library second only to what we had. Pergamum has lost importance as a city; few scholars visit that library. It is becoming an unused, buried treasure. Will you give me the scrolls and books from Pergamum to take back to Alexandria?"

He shook his head admiringly. "I would have expected you to ask for jewels. You shall have your gift. I will rob Pergamum of its treasures for you."

They were riding back from this fishing expedition when one of his officers came up and drew him aside. Cleopatra waited. She guessed, from the glances that Anthony gave her, that their conversation was of her. Whatever it was, it obviously worried Anthony.

He left the officer and rode to her side.

"I have unpleasant news. My troops have captured a young woman in Miletus. She was stirring up trouble there, claiming to be your sister and the rightful queen of Egypt. She was demanding help to march against you. Do you wish to see her?"

"Arsinoë! I heard she escaped from Rome during the turmoil after Caesar's death. No, I do not want to see her."

"Then," he said, "I shall keep her and take her back with me when I return to Rome."

She moved closer to him and put her hand on his arm. "You asked me what gift I wanted. I will give up the library of Pergamum if you will grant me another, instead. For my sake be merciful. Have her quickly put to death. I cannot bear that she should once again be dragged in shame behind a Roman chariot. She is a little mad by now, I think, but she is still a Ptolemy."

Cleopatra had no feeling for her sister. After all these years Arsinoë was only a name to her—but that name was Ptolemy.

"You constantly surprise me," he answered her. "Just now you spoke and thought as a Roman would. Better a quick death than years of shame and dishonor! You shall have both requests."

The next day it was her turn to be surprised. He decided not to wait but to go with her now to Alexandria. He could not bear to be separated from her.

They arrived in Alexandria to find serious problems. The Nile River had been perilously low that year. It had not overflown its banks as usual and the green valley had shrunk. Egypt was faced with drought and famine.

The Queen's first act was to announce the suspension of many taxes. Without the burden of taxes the farmers could well survive until the river rose again. The people blessed Cleopatra, and she made it clear that Anthony was their benefactor. As one of the consuls of Rome he had declared that no tribute need go to Rome, and thus the taxes could be suspended.

They were such a handsome couple together that their romance was a legend come to life, and they were swept up into the nation's adulation. The Alexandrians adored them. Anthony's joyous love of amusements suited them far more than had Caesar's frugal way of life. He was as lighthearted as they, by nature.

Although Anthony was forty-two, he belonged in the company

of younger men. He taught the Queen how to be young. The two of them became the leaders of a pleasure-seeking, though harmless, group of youths who thought nothing of staying up all night over a banquet, watching their favorite dancers or listening to their favorite singers, and then starting out on a wild chariot race in the morning.

She made up now for all the years when she had had no youth and no leisure for enjoyment. Her imagination was quicker than the others. It was she who would suddenly propose a midnight swim in the harbor or a masquerade when they would disguise themselves as street musicians or a sunrise boating expedition on Lake Mareotis. It was she who had merchants bring her, from every part of Asia Minor, the newest acrobats, magicians and entertainers for Anthony's amusement.

But if she had been only a playmate, he would soon have tired of her as he had of other women. What bound him to her more closely every day were the many-sided surprises of her personality.

When he arose at noon, he found she had already spent hours of hard work with her government council. When he was surfeited with too much light pleasure, he found she had anticipated his boredom and had arranged for a quiet evening with the scholars of the museum university. If, at times, he grew too confident of her love and assumed a Roman arrogance, she became contrary and did nothing he wanted.

"Why are you dressed in your royal robes? You know I have arranged that we hunt today. You cannot ride in that robe," he objected.

"I am not in the mood to hunt. Today Caesarion and I attend the play in the theatre," she answered.

Scowling, he refused to believe her. "Last night you said the play would be dull. Why must you play tricks like this?"

"Because I have changed my mind." And off she went to the theatre, leaving him to spend the day without her. While the chorus was singing, Charmian whispered: "Are you not afraid to offend him? That is surely not the way to hold a man's love. Don't you care to please him?"

"I please myself and that intrigues him. You will see."

She was right. When they returned from the play it was to find a sulky but chastened Anthony, who had had a miserable day without her.

Saat worried for her. "Perhaps I am too old to understand, Cleopatra, but I fear that you are taxing your strength and energy. You never neglect Caesarion or the affairs of your kingdom, yet these parties, these trips and adventures, these amusements must rob you of sleep and rest which you need."

"I have two secrets and I shall tell them only to you," she said tenderly to the elderly little man who had stood by her in so many difficult situations. "I have the reputation of being able to drink wine long after even Anthony is drunk, but my cup is always brought to me by one steward, who is too loyal to betray me. In my cup the wine is mostly water. And my second secret is Anthony, himself. I love him most dearly, Saat. I have never been so well, so alive, so stimulated in heart and spirit as I am with him."

The whole winter went by in this newfound happiness. It could not last nor had she expected that Anthony would stay with her forever.

By spring, matters in Rome had come to such a difficult pass that his presence there was essential. The quarreling between Fulvia and Octavian was driving the country to an ugly division. Anthony wanted peace, so that he could carry out Caesar's great ambition to bring Persia into the empire of Rome.

The two lovers said good-by without tears. They thought they would see each other soon again, when Anthony had straightened out affairs at home.

It was now the year 40 B.C. and Cleopatra was twenty-nine. That summer she gave birth to twins. Anthony's son she named Alexander and his daughter was given the favorite Ptolemaic name of Cleopatra. She loved them both but neither could push out Caesarion from the place he occupied in her heart.

At seven Caesarion was growing tall, straight and strong, with a well-coordinated body. He was beginning to learn the things a young prince should learn. Because of his mother's watchfulness he had escaped completely the willful, cruel, petulant temper of so many of the Ptolemies. He inherited Caesar's stability. It was too early to know if he had Caesar's talent for leadership.

The months went by. What she heard from Rome first made her uneasy, then filled her with miserable foreboding.

Fulvia and Octavian had, indeed, embroiled Rome in senseless quarrels—most of which were Fulvia's fault. Octavian had become so angry at her ridiculous behavior that he had repudiated his marriage to her daughter, and had then married Scribonia, the niece of Sextus Pompeius.

Anthony was forced to take Fulvia's side. He gathered together his legions and prepared to advance south of Rome toward Sicily, where Octavian and Sextus were.

At that fateful moment Fulvia fell suddenly ill and died.

Peace was arranged between Anthony and Octavian. It was a peace forced upon them, demanded by the weary, war-sick citizens of Italy.

All of this Cleopatra learned from her messengers, but very little from Anthony. At first she told herself that he was too busy to write often, but as time went by and peace came to Rome, she did not have this excuse.

Then word came that Anthony had married Octavian's sister, Octavia.

Cleopatra wept and could not be consoled. She shut herself away from everyone, even from her children. She knew that the marriage was certainly a matter of civic policy, a tie to bind Anthony and Octavian together. Just the same, Octavia was young and pretty, and Anthony liked pretty women.

It took a long time for the violence of her grief to pass. Even then she took up her duties with a dull, constant ache in her heart. She cared more deeply for Anthony than she had realized.

Reason told her it was better for Egypt that matters had turned out this way. Anthony would not forget her. He would always think of her tenderly. He would not let any greedy Roman Senate get control of Egypt; that much he would do for her.

Since they were separated, his enemies and hers could make no trouble for either of them. She was not now coming between a Roman husband and wife. She was not the foreign enchantress who lured men to their downfall.

Reason was small comfort. She did her best to present a serene and quiet face to her children, her attendants and her ministers, but it was a hard-won serenity.

Three years went by. She devoted herself to the care of her children. Under her guidance Egypt continued to prosper. It surprised her that she was more attractive to men than ever, because she thought she had put all such ideas of love and romance out of her life. If she could not have Anthony she wanted no one else.

She worked so hard and so well that her people began to regard her as truly the incarnation of the mother-goddess Isis. More and more, throughout Egypt, they were naming her "Cleopatra the Great," or simply calling her "Egypt," thus honoring her the more.

But in her own chambers she overheard Charmian sadly say to Iras, "I like it not. I would rather she would be angry with me or scold me, than to be so good. I fear her spirit is broken." And, overhearing, the Queen was not angry. It was too near the truth.

She was totally unprepared in the year 36 B.C. for the messenger who came to her from Syria and for the letter he brought. It was from Anthony. He had come to Syria to prepare at last for the Persian campaign. He wanted her. He had never stopped loving her. Would she not forgive his silences and come to him now?

When she put down the letter after reading it and looked up at Charmian, it was as if the three years had never passed. Her eyes were blazing; her face was alive with color and animation. True, it was partly with anger, but Charmian rejoiced to see it.

"Tell me what news, Cleopatra—" she began.

"He wants me to come! After three years of absence and neglect he expects to beckon to me and I am to hasten to him, like any lovesick girl!" the Queen raged. "I shall not go."

"Of course not," Charmian soothed her. "Octavia is in Athens. Let him bring her on to Syria to comfort him. Let her amuse him and be entertained and loved by him."

"Stop! Do not speak of her. Where is Appolodorus? Why is he never here when I want him? I must have the swiftest ship. I must sail tomorrow without fail. Every minute of delay is torture." She was almost frantic. "Prepare my clothes. Bring my jewel cases. Hurry!"

In the midst of the turmoil of her packing and of taking leave of her children, Saat appeared to beg for an urgent audience with her.

"You must not go. Have you taken leave of your senses? Queen Cleopatra, you endanger everything you and I have worked for: the safety of Egypt. If you step between Octavia and Anthony, you will incur the deadly hatred of the wife's brother, Octavian. By this act you will place the lives and the freedom of us all, in jeopardy."

"I cannot help it," she cried. "Do you think I can always be the queen and never just the woman? Besides, Anthony will protect us."

Saat was a stern judge. He was unmoved by her tears. "Once before, you placed all your trust in a Roman and were betrayed. I defended and upheld you then because you did what was right. It was not your fault he betrayed you and Caesarion. But if you go now to Syria, I ask permission to withdraw from your Council."

It was a serious and tragic break between them. She was sorry but she could no more resist going to Syria than she could stop breathing.

She sailed the next day. Only one ship went this time, the fastest that could be found. And when she came in sight of the city of Antioch she found that she was more than welcomed and expected: sentries posted on every height of land signaled her coming; she was met at the dock by courtiers and escorted, riding a magnificent brocaded litter, to the palatial home where Anthony made his headquarters.

When she saw him she knew that all her fears were groundless. He had never stopped loving her; he had never loved her more than now.

"You never forgot me?" she asked.

"Not for a single moment." He held her fiercely, yet tenderly. "I tried to. Duty is inbred in every Roman. It was my duty to make the peace my country wanted and the marriage my country demanded. Octavia is sweet and good. I would have liked to have pleased her. But it is my fate to love you as no man has ever loved a woman before."

She was struck by something different in him. The three years had been no easier for him than for her. In the process of time a certain shallow lightness in him had been refined away. His feelings were deeper, more honest, more sincere.

He proved to her that he had spoken the truth. He told her that just after he married Octavia he had secretly made his last will and testament and given it to the Supreme Vestal of the Vestal Virgins to keep. In that will he had ordered that when he died his body was to be taken to Alexandria and buried by the side of the tomb of Queen Cleopatra.

She knew that she should never have doubted him. He might be fickle in small matters, but when he loved it was with a fanatical constancy. As he had been constant to Caesar so he would be constant to her.

But he was also constant to his old, reckless, impetuous nature. She could hardly believe it when she heard his decision.

"I shall never return to Octavia. Perhaps I shall never again return to Rome, not even to visit. Octavian and I have reaffirmed our division of territory and mine is all of the East. When I have conquered in Persia I will control lands so vast, my armies will be so strong and so well repaid, so loyal to me, that Octavian will not dare to challenge anything I do. Let him have Rome and the West. My kingdom will be here, lying next to yours. I cut myself off forever from Rome and Octavia."

"Then, Anthony, cut the ties with Rome cleanly. I insist that we be married."

He was even more eager for the ceremony than she. And after the marriage he made her an incredible gift: the whole Roman province of Lebanon, the peninsula of Sinai, part of Petra and Samaria and Galilee and Crete, all were hers as a wedding present.

Although once again there were amusements and parties, they were fewer and quieter. Anthony was in the midst of all the preparations for his campaign, training his soldiers, and when he had any spare time he was content to be alone with his wife. They were so happy they were radiant with it; so wrapped up in each other he was loath to tear himself away for the Persian campaign.

All too soon he had to go. She rode with him as far as the Euphrates River. There they separated. She watched him as he rode ahead of his great army, proudly loving his handsome and valorous figure. Then she turned her own caravan to cross over-land through Jericho, Sinai and the Red Sea and return to Egypt.

In Alexandria the news of her marriage was proclaimed, as well as the news that Egypt had acquired new lands and provinces. She summoned Saat.

"Will you not admit, now, that you were wrong?" she begged him. "Listen to those shouts and cheers from the city! Without a sword raised, without the loss of a single Egyptian life, I have expanded our kingdom to a greatness it has not known in centuries. With Anthony as Autocrator of the rest of the East, we have carved up this part of the world between us. The eastern Mediterranean is our private lake. Will you still say I was wrong to go to Anthony?"

"You and Marc Anthony are like children playing with bubbles," he answered, unsmiling and sorrowful. "You shut your eyes and try to believe that Octavian, too, is a child like yourselves. You forget that he has grown in strength, wisdom and power. He is the best administrator, lawmaker and judge, in his cold way, that Rome has ever had. Do you think he will allow Anthony to set up his own empire out of what were once Roman lands? Do you think he will be content that Egypt shall have the riches of Lebanon and Crete? Do not boast, Queen Cleopatra, that you have won these without raising a sword. You have not won them at all. They are bright-colored bubbles in your hands."

"You are a stupid, opinionated, senile old man!" she screamed at him. "Get out. Get out of my sight!—no, come back, come back, Saat!" She reached out to stop him but he was gone.

While Anthony was in Persia and she waited in Alexandria, the temptation to believe in her own future and to discount Saat's warnings was great. New wealth poured into Egypt. She sent governors out to the new provinces, and the tribute money came to her instead of to Rome. Ships and trading were diverted to Alexandria instead of to Italy. The rich businessmen of Egypt grew richer; trading expanded. Employment grew and she was the great Queen who was blessed for it.

But she could not shake off the foreboding Saat had brought her. A feeling of imminent disaster stayed with her night and day.

Then Anthony's galley ships came at last into the harbor. They crept in. They were silent ships. No victorious army from on board cheered the sight of land. There was something dispirited, beaten, about them.

A soldier, thin and gaunt, came to tell her the truth.

Anthony had been defeated in Persia. He and his soldiers had had to retreat. They had been cut off from the baggage wagons. They had starved; they had eaten poisoned weeds and many had died; they had reached Syria with hardly any clothes on their backs and no shoes on their feet.

"Why did he not come to Alexandria with you?" she asked.

The soldier's eyes filled with tears. "He would not leave the sick and the wounded. He shared our sufferings. He ate no more than we did. He loaned his horse to the wounded and he walked with us, on foot. The men in Syria, Queen Cleopatra, have no food and no clothing. Anthony could not leave them."

Once more, in this late spring of 35 B.C., she sailed with a fleet to be with Anthony. This time, however, her ships carried no silks or jewels or flower gardens. They were loaded with money for food and with clothing for the army.

TEN

WHEN SHE saw Anthony she hardly knew him. His giant frame was all skin and bones. He had rarely slept. He spent his time going from tent to tent to care for his sick and dying.

That night she held him close while he told her the terrible story and confessed his own bewilderment at what had happened.

"It was winter but I thought it was the best time to strike; strike hard and fast when they were not expecting us to move. We went on forced marches, the legions and I. Everything melted away in front of us. There was no resistance. So I forced the march even faster and left the baggage wagons behind. I thought we could live off the country. Roman armies have done that before. But we also had to leave behind the siege implements, the battering rams and the catapults. I did not expect the capital city of Media to hold out."

Unbidden, to her mind came the thought that Caesar would have anticipated this. He would have prepared for the *worst* conditions. Anthony looked for the best.

She said nothing and he went on, not sparing himself, "There was no wood around Media. We could not make battering rams. The city could not be taken. All the food was in there; the countryside was stripped. We were outside, thousands of us, with no food and shelter. Finally we had to retreat. The enemy followed, striking at the stragglers and the rear guard. Starvation and thirst sent my army into flight toward safety and water."

She spoke softly and tenderly to him, "Do not remember it any more. We will rebuild your army with Egyptian gold and you will come back and win in Persia."

He took heart from her. Comforted, he slept well for the first time in a month.

She could not sleep. She had to face the fact that Saat had been right and, politically, she had made a tragic mistake. She had linked Egypt's fate to a man whose star of fortune was falling. Anthony was no Caesar. He was no cool-headed, sober planner as Caesar had been. He was dashing, swaggering, reckless and bold. Put an enemy in front of him and an open field for an open fight and no one could withstand the courage of Anthony. Put him behind a table with papers and maps, to plan sieges and encirclements and day-by-day strategy, with problems of food supply and water replenishments—and Anthony was lost.

The same weaknesses that had lost him Persia would render him helpless in the political game for power with Octavian.

As Queen, she could admit her mistake; but as a woman she knew it would have been impossible for her to have stayed away from Anthony.

They remained there only long enough to see his soldiers cared for with money, food, clothing and physicians, then the two of them went back to Alexandria.

His pride was so broken that it would have been easy for Anthony to yield to the temptations of that city and become nothing but an idler. It was to his credit as a man that he thought only of redeeming himself. She was clever enough to help him. Wisely, she counseled him not to try the impossible. Persia was impregnable as long as the King of the Medes was Persia's ally. The best plan was a flanking one: to march against the King of Armenia, conquer him and so frighten the King of the Medes that a treaty could be made. Leave Persia for another year.

So in the spring, Anthony again took the field with his legions. Everything went as they had planned. His victories were small ones, but not easy ones, and he emerged from them with the treaty that separated the Medes and the Persians, with his army heartened and strong. When he came back to Alexandria, Anthony was his old blithe, confident, boisterous self.

He swung Iras and Charmian high up in his arms. He had presents for his own two children as well as for Caesarion. He swaggered before Cleopatra, the conquering hero, and she rejoiced to see him like this once more.

The Persian campaign was never mentioned again. Anthony's ambitions were at an end. Tribute money poured in from all the lands of which he was now styled "Autocrator"; his legions settled down, happily, well-paid, to marry women in Syria, in Antioch and in Egypt. Rome was far away and too sick of the long civil wars between, first, Caesar and Pompey, then, Anthony and Brutus, to do more than murmur against Anthony's actions.

Anthony had everything he wanted and was happy with it.

But the Queen was not fooled. She knew that Octavian would not forever let things rest as they were. On the surface, the next four years of Cleopatra's life were gloriously trouble-free and joyous. She kept her own counsel. No one knew that she awoke each morning wondering if disaster would strike that day.

So she lived each month, each week, day and hour, as if it were her last. She had never been more vividly alive. In the mornings, just the sight from her window of the sun striking and coloring the waters of the harbor was enough to gladden her. She never tired of visiting and revisiting all the places she loved: the museum, the library, the theatre, the Pharos Lighthouse, the royal pavilions. To be carried through the Street of Canopus on her litter was as exciting as if she were doing it for the first time.

If Anthony rode with her, he found her unpredictable. One

moment she would insist on stopping in the street to buy sweet-
meats from a peddler or to watch a shabby fire-swallower entertain a crowd at a street corner or to smile at children playing
a game. The next moment the curtains of her litter would close
and she would not even speak to him. He did not know that
behind those curtains she cried because all these things were
precious to her and she knew she would be losing them one day.

If she went out with Caesarion she did not cry. She made him
see everything, impressing upon him that the street peddler and
the fire-swallower were as much his duty to protect as the wealthi-
est Alexandrian merchant. She wanted him to see everything
through her eyes. The people, too, must see Caesarion and give
him their allegiance.

While Anthony was fighting in Armenia she had given birth
to another son, Ptolemy. When she celebrated Anthony's triumph, Ptolemy and her twins each had a small throne. But
Caesarion's throne was next to hers, and he wore the crown as
she did.

That celebration was a substitute for the Day of Triumph
Anthony would have had in Rome. In the vast stadium she had
had the thrones erected with all of the glitter of gold and silks
and peacock fans so dear to the hearts of the luxury-loving Alexandrians. The immense crowd liked this new spectacle. They
thrilled to the blaring of trumpets and watched the procession
with delighted eyes. It marked Anthony's triumph over Armenia,
and it displayed all the loot of goods from that country.

At the proper moment Anthony rode his chariot around, to
the frenzied cheers of the Alexandrians. He dismounted before
the Queen and strode up to take his place beside her.

The spectacle was repeated again, a few days later. But this
time Anthony stood below the Queen and Caesarion, and below
the tiny thrones of his children. He was declaring the rights of
succession.

Once more Cleopatra saw and heard Anthony's remarkable voice hold a crowd spellbound.

This day, he said, meant "a new era, opened by Cleopatra, Queen of Egypt, Cyprus and Syria. He who stands before you," and Anthony turned slightly and with a motion of his hand indicated the tall and straight-standing Caesarion, "Caesar Ptolemy, is today elevated to the rank of 'King of Kings,' as co-regent with his mother over Egypt."

He had to wait until the cheers subsided, then he went on to declare that his own son, little Alexander, was now named King of Armenia. The twin sister, Cleopatra, would be Queen of Lydia. The baby Ptolemy was the future King of Phoenicia and Cilicia.

Not only Alexandria, but the whole of Egypt went mad with joy. Anthony had officially cut off those countries and provinces from Rome. Henceforth, the Ptolemaic line would rule among them a vast empire of the whole eastern Mediterranean. Public banquets were given by Cleopatra so that in every city and town the people of Egypt were holiday-makers, wining and dining at the expense of the royal treasury.

It seemed as if not only a new era, but a Golden Era, was opening up before Cleopatra and her children. But in Rome Octavian was also giving free banquets. The Roman people were truly hungry. For four years they had been deprived of the wealth of the East. Actual starvation faced them.

It had taken Octavian those full four years to undermine the popularity of Anthony. Now, both in sorrow and anger, the Romans were coming to feel that Anthony was a traitor and a renegade who cared nothing for their hunger so long as he could feast by the side of Cleopatra. They were ready to move. If they were to keep the prosperity they were accustomed to, they would have to put on soldiers' uniforms once more and move against Anthony.

All of this Cleopatra read in the reports she had received. And when she at last heard that Octavian was building up his army to its full strength of thirty legions, she knew it was time for Anthony to prepare.

He heard the news scornfully. Because they were both highly charged, dynamic people he and Cleopatra quarreled often. This was an epic quarrel. Downstairs in the kitchens the slaves cowered while Cleopatra and Anthony raged and stormed from chamber to chamber, hallways and stairs, audience hall and gardens.

"I welcome the chance to meet that coward! Do you think I am afraid of him?" they could hear Anthony's roaring bass voice flinging a challenge to the Queen. "I will wipe him from the face of the earth!"

She taunted him, jeered at him, cajoled him, flung goading words at his head. "Do you think Octavian and you will be meeting in single combat? It is his brains you should fear—that, and the hungry stomachs of the Roman soldiers. Oh, why did you not kill Octavian at Philippi? How could you let him live? Anthony, you must not treat this so lightly. This coming battle will decide our lives. Are you so stupid you do not see that?"

"Are you as fainthearted as all other women? Afraid of a mouse? That's what Octavian is. That is why I didn't kill him at Philippi, because I do not hunt down mice. I will meet this new army of his and then you will prepare for me a great Day of Triumph—and, perhaps," he grumbled, "I will forgive you then for your lack of faith in me."

"I do not lack faith in your bravery. Only in your judgment!" she flashed at him. "There is still time to train as many recruits as Octavian has legions. I wish I had been born a man!"

"I don't." He threw back his head and laughed, caught her in an embrace, and the quarrel was over. When he departed for Ephesus, to gather up all the recruits and whatever he could of his old legions, he told her with a deep sincerity, "You will follow me. You will witness this battle. If, by accident such as will happen to any soldier, I am captured, then I will kill myself.

Promise me to bring my body back here. When you die, let our tombs be side by side."

"If you die, Anthony, then I shall kill myself," she answered.

He looked at her with awe. "I believe that you would."

It was several months later that she came to Ephesus, in Greece, where he was encamped. She brought with her gold to buy new recruits and great quantities of supplies for them, as well as a few comforts for Anthony. She came, full of hope, but her heart sank at what she saw.

Anthony had worked hard and intensely, but carelessly. He drove himself night and day to teach his motley army of Armenians, Syrians, Egyptians, Greeks and others how to fight with shield and sword but he had not instituted discipline. Off-duty, his new soldiers drank and caroused. The tents were not neat and orderly lines. They straggled off and were dirty. Women and peddlers, gamblers and entertainers had flocked around to keep the men amused and take their money.

Anthony, at last, was facing his situation and knew the outlook was dark. "Four hundred Romans of senatorial rank," he told her, soberly, "left Rome to join me here because they feared Octavian is planning to make himself emperor. He has forced everyone to swear allegiance to him personally, not to the standards. These four hundred men could have been the officers of my army and put discipline into this rabble. However, I found they came here expecting me to deny all of Octavian's charges—"

"And you cannot deny them." She was calm.

"No. They want me to repudiate you, go back to Rome, take away all the lands and countries I have given you and see that their wealth comes again into the port of Ostia. They declare you a witch and a sorceress."

She put her hand on his but he withdrew it. He walked to a window where he could see the hot Grecian sun beat down on the ground beneath. Against such a light she could only see him as a dark and powerful figure. A stranger. Her heart was hammering. Would Anthony yield now and declare as his excuse that she had bewitched him?

He was speaking in a low and terrible voice, "They say I deserted Rome. I was trained to consider my country more dear than fame or wealth—or a woman. I gave up these ideals because I loved you."

"Do you regret it, Anthony? Would you have done differently? It is not too late. You can give assurances to these senators. You can go back to Rome and make peace with Octavian."

Slowly he turned his back to the window and came to her. He stood looking down; he brushed aside a curl that fell on her forehead. His hand gently slid along the curve of her cheek. "It is too late. I could never repudiate you. If I die tomorrow I have known a happiness that few mortals have ever known. They can write on my epitaph: *Fortunate was Anthony, beloved of Cleopatra!*"

Even when the four hundred senators left him in disgust, he kept his cheerfulness and his courage. He threw himself into the work of training raw recruits and in planning the strategy with his newly created officers. His strength of mind was so great it withstood all pressure. When an old friend of his, Geminius, came at great risk to beg him to renounce Cleopatra, Anthony struck the table with his fist, roaring at Geminius to be gone.

He wrote Octavian a letter, though he knew that letter would be read aloud to Roman citizens. He meant it for their ears. The letter said: "What has put you out of temper with me? That I sleep with the Queen? She is my wife. Is that anything new? She has been my wife for nine years now. . . ."

Formally and tardily, he divorced Octavia.

Cleopatra saw that he smiled and laughed, that he joked with his men, that he seemed to be without care, and she admired him more in these last, tragic moments than she had ever before. He knew what his chances were. Octavian was sending his best general, Agrippa, and Agrippa was not walking into any trap on the

Ephesian mainland. The Roman ships waited outside the port, daring Anthony to come out.

"Will you fight him at sea?" she asked anxiously. "Your men are trained for land battles, not sea warfare."

Over his face had come a hardening of resolve, but his tone was somber and fatalistic. She knew that the attitude of those four hundred senators had badly shaken his confidence in his future. "I must fight now. We cannot argue with the gods, Cleopatra. They have withdrawn their favor from me. My camp has been stricken by disease. If I wait and hope to draw Agrippa to the land, I will not have enough healthy soldiers left to fight him. I have no choice."

The night before the battle they both tried to smile and laugh and tease each other but their merriment was hollow. They fell silent, sitting with clasped hands, listening to the soft sounds of a lute player. The music was haunting, sad, nostalgic.

They had faced battles before, but they had been younger and reckless. Tonight fate seemed to brood over them. She said, gently, "You must sleep, Anthony. You must not think of me."

He lifted her hand to his lips. "Tomorrow I will forget you and I will see Agrippa's face, not yours, and hear his war cries and not your lovely voice. I may die tomorrow and sleep forever. Let us not think of sleep now."

The next morning all was bustle and shouted orders and the blare of trumpets, as his soldiers crowded on board the Grecian galleys. Anthony was in the foremost vessel. Cleopatra was to go with the war fleet but her small, fast ship was ordered to stay far in the rear. As she stood on deck she could see Anthony, in full armor, his face and eyes alight with the joy of danger, standing in the prow of his enormous galley. He shouted something to the helmsman; he turned and motioned to the ships following his. Then he was lost to her sight as the fleet moved northward out of the bay.

Her own ship sailed just close enough so that she could see

the tops of the enemy masts outside of the Gulf of Ambracia off
the promontory of Actium. From then on the joining of the battle
as the two fleets came together was a series of terrible and uncon-
nected pictures before her eyes.

Anthony's big war-galley bore down on the little ships of
Agrippa's and scattered them, but she could not tell what was
happening. She sent crewmen up to the very tops of her sail masts
to give her reports.

At first those reports were favorable. A crewman slid down
and told her, panting with haste and effort, "Our lord Anthony's
ships are the biggest. He plunges against them like a bear against
dogs!"

But he could not ram them. His big ship was clumsy. The
little ones of Agrippa could dart in again and again, to throw
spears and burning brands and get away before Anthony could
maneuver to ram and board them.

The bear was being swarmed over by the dogs.

She could hear the shouts, the screams, the crash of timbers.
She could see the smoke of burning ships. With face white and
strained and with eyes desperate to find out the truth, she clung to
the rail of her ship and tried to understand what was happening.

Then, out of the clouds of smoke, she saw one of the big ships
drifting back, helpless and disabled. It was on fire. It was not
Anthony's galley, but it was the portent of how the battle was
going. Anthony's soldiers were inept. They had never been trained
to fight at sea. His ships were too big and awkward. Agrippa, her
watchers in the masts reported, had five ships to every one of
Anthony's, and five small ships could surround one big galley
and throw burning arrows into the wood and lances into human
flesh—and then scurry off before the galley could come close.

It was defeat. One after another she saw the ships of Anthony's
fleet float by, wrecked, burning, helpless, dying.

She waited only until she realized that Anthony was fighting
the whole of the enemy, alone. Surrender or death was certain.

Then she moved. Swiftly she gave orders for full sail. Hers was a fast vessel. With no fear for her own personal safety she had her captain fly into the very thick of what was left of the fight and maneuver as close to Anthony's galley as possible.

She saw him now and her heart almost broke. He was besieged. Some of Agrippa's men had actually got on board. Sword in hand, he fought them, standing them off. He was outnumbered. He was giving way but fighting desperately over the deck slippery with blood and sea water.

He raised his head and saw her ship and her signal. He understood. He shouted to his own men and, as her ship veered close against his, Anthony and a dozen of his men leaped to the railings and then for her rope ladders, to safety. By a miracle, the captain of Cleopatra's ship had come up so fast that he had caught the enemy unaware, and they could not stop the rescue.

Not understanding what was happening, Agrippa's ships had scattered for the moment. It was just time enough for the Egyptian ship to slip past them all and make for the open sea.

The pursuit could not catch up. They were safe. They made straight for Alexandria.

But Anthony cried out to her in a terrible voice: "I should have stayed! I should have died there with the rest." He slumped, exhausted and beaten, onto a bench and stayed there. She knew better than to speak to him or touch him. He was alone in the terrible agony of defeat.

In Alexandria he recovered enough to present a brave face to the outside world. But they were both doomed people, Anthony and Cleopatra, and they knew it. The mark of death was on them. Octavian's forces would now come to Egypt.

There were things she must do. She must send Caesarion away into the desert, where she had once gone for safety. She must humble herself and see old Saat. "You must help me, not for my sake but Caesarion's. I will hide him. After my death you must take over the government and bargain as best you can with Octavian for the freedom of Egypt and the right of Caesarion to rule."

He agreed.

Anthony, too, felt this was the best move. "Octavian may take pity on the three children who are mine, for the sake of my ancestors. It is not uncommon. Children of enemies are frequently taken back to Rome and given to relatives to rear. It is Caesarion whom Octavian will kill."

So she sent Caesarion away, after a farewell which was heartrending. The mother and her seventeen-year-old son embraced without tears, without words, too moved to speak. Only as she watched him go out of the gates of the palace with his escort, did she break into a cry. She turned and clung to Anthony.

There was so little time left. They spent it together. They designed their two tombs which would be side by side, and they watched the building of them. The final resting place for their bodies was important. Cleopatra, even though Greek by birth, had adopted much of the Egyptian religion, which laid particular emphasis on the tombs of kings and queens.

Saat asked for a private audience with her. "Anthony will die." He was ruthless with her. "But is there no way in which you could bargain with this Octavian? You are clever. You must stay alive. Let him take you in chains if he wishes, so long as he grants Caesarion the right to life and the throne."

"You cannot ask that of me!" she cried.

"I do ask it. I demand it. You made the mistake. You should pay. Not Caesarion." For all his age he was strong still.

She bowed her head and wept. "You are right, Saat. I will do it, but say nothing to Anthony."

She felt his hand on her head, stroking it gently. He said, "You have been as my daughter. I have loved you more than anyone, even my gods. You were a great queen, Cleopatra. When I was a young man I thought it was inevitable that the tide of Rome would sweep over us. Then you came to the throne and, alone and singlehanded, held back that tide for us. What a tragedy that you should be punished for having a woman's heart!'"

With a tremendous force of men behind him, Octavian marched across Sinai and swept up to the gates of Alexandria. Anthony sent him a challenge to a single combat duel but it was refused. The battle began.

At first it seemed as if their fears were wrong. In the first charges Anthony and his few troops were victorious. He was fighting like a madman, with a resurgence of his old power. He was laughing as he fought, shouting his old battle cries. Men fell in fright before him. His giant figure was something more than human.

In full armor, Cleopatra watched from a height. Almost, she dared let herself hope. There was a singing and a clamor in her veins as she saw the titanic, splendid struggle of Anthony.

But by the second day the force of numbers pressed him back—back and back, and finally into the city. The gates were closed. They were besieged for a while; then traitors opened the gates to Octavian.

Anthony sent Cleopatra back to the palace. "Stay there," he urged. "If you get word of my death you will know what to do."

Street by street, foot by foot, he made the Roman legions fight for the city. Both sides were exhausted. Yet Anthony might have won, by the sheer daring of his leadership, if he had not been betrayed.

His men on board the ships in the harbor deserted. His captains on land went over to Octavian. They were Romans who resented that they fought their fellow Romans for the sake of an Egyptian queen. Anthony found himself almost alone, and, in his despair, he thought that Cleopatra had sold out to Octavian, bargaining for her own safety.

He rushed to the palace but he was greeted there by servants and slaves running about in a frenzy, weeping and wailing. When he stopped one and demanded, "Where is the Queen? What has happened?" the answer he got was, "She is dead! She has killed herself because a report came that you were slain."

Without a moment's hesitation Anthony plunged his sword into his breast. He was dying, but because of the enormous strength of his great frame, he managed to stagger out into the gardens where their two huge mausoleums had been built. Anthony wept because of his belief that she had betrayed him, when instead she had killed herself.

She heard him coming. She was not dead. It was true that she had heard the false report and then carried out her own plans. With Iras and Charmian she had gone to her mausoleum and entered the building. Appolodorus had then sealed up the door, leaving only a small opening in the roof for light and air.

Now from inside she could hear Anthony's voice, crying for her. It was weak and full of pain.

"Anthony! They told me you were slain." Their voices were faint to each other but clear, as he called out her name. She pressed herself against the wall nearest him. It was agony to know that he was still alive, so close that she could almost touch him.

But Appolodorus was there. "He is dying, Egypt."

"Bring him to me, in the tomb. Carry him up over the roof and down through the opening," she commanded.

So Appolodorus bore the dying body of Anthony in his arms up to the top of the mausoleum and lowered it carefully to the arms of the three women inside. Sitting on the ground, the Queen cradled Anthony's head in her lap and mourned only for him, forgetting for a little while the fate that was threatening her.

In these last seconds of his life Anthony was more noble than he had ever been. "Do not weep, Cleopatra," he whispered. "Rejoice, rather, in the remembrance of my past happiness than bewail my present misfortunes. In life I was illustrious and my death is not inglorious. I have always conquered as a Roman; it is only by a Roman that I am conquered."

Then he died.

The Roman soldiers of Octavian found her still sitting beside Anthony. They broke in the door. Dazed by her sorrow over Anthony, she was not quick enough with her own dagger and it was seized from her hand before she could stab herself with it. The soldiers handled her roughly. They searched her for other weapons, holding her hands over her head, treating her as if her royal dignity were a thing of the past.

Though the door was now opened, she remained in her tomb, awaiting the pleasure of Octavian.

Octavian sent messages: if she would come out of her own accord and yield herself his prisoner, she would be treated as a queen. He threatened her. If she killed herself he would kill the three children he had found in her palace.

Cleopatra trusted neither his promises nor his threats. She had one thing left with which to bargain for the safety of Caesarion and her other children, and for the dignity of her own death. With her in the mausoleum were most of her treasures of jewels and gold; she alone knew where the rest were hidden.

The last messenger was Dolabella. He had hated Anthony but he had always admired Cleopatra. Now he yielded to pity and he whispered to her the truth: Octavian would treat her as a queen, yes—but a conquered queen, to be dragged behind his chariot in his triumph in Rome. No matter what she did he would not spare Caesarion. Her son would be hunted down and killed.

With that, her last reason for living was gone. She could only play for time in order to somehow secure a sword, a dagger or another weapon.

Octavian came. She was on her bed, feigning illness. She asked of him two favors: that he would give her lord Anthony a royal burial and that she might be allowed to see her physician, Olympus. Octavian agreed, impatient to get to the inventory of her jewels.

The body of Anthony was taken away. Olympus came. While the Queen's steward busied himself showing Octavian the lists of the treasure and while Octavian's eyes were fixed on such dazzling wealth, Cleopatra had a moment to whisper a request of her physician and see his understanding nod.

Beside her Iras and Charmian wept. They were heartbroken to see their proud mistress brought so low, so ill. Her hair was disheveled. Her face was bathed in perspiration. She clung to Olympus for a second before she let him go, and fell back again on her pillow. The two loyal maids were furious that this Octavian should so desecrate a mausoleum that he would enter it and rifle it of its treasures. In the Egyptian religion a dead king or queen always kept his most precious jewels and articles of gold with him because they would be used and needed in the after-life as much as in this one.

As Octavian was leaving he came to her couch and asked after her health. Had her physician given her a good remedy?

She understood his anxiety. He wanted her well, so that she could go back to Rome and walk in chains behind his chariot. She smiled at him. Yes, the physician had given her a remedy. Would Octavian allow food and wine to be sent in to the mausoleum? The Queen would rise and dress herself, eat and drink.

Octavian was satisfied. He gave orders that a banquet be sent in, past the guards at her door.

Cleopatra rose. Her pretended illness fell away from her. She saw the shocked and scandalized looks on the faces of Iras and Charmian as she gave orders: "My finest robes—my crown—my jewels. Prepare my bath."

Because an Egyptian tomb was considered the dwelling place of the dead, who behaved in death as they did in life, there were baths and beds, couches and tables in the beautiful prison where they were.

The wine and the food came, and the three women ate and drank. The meal was almost over when they heard the guard outside the door questioning someone.

"What have you in your basket, old woman?" he demanded.

"Just some figs for the poor, sick Queen, sir," came the halting answer outside the door. "Just something sent to tempt the appetite. It is the physician's orders."

The door was partly open and Cleopatra saw the guard handle the top row of figs in the basket. She held her breath in fright. She prayed to her gods that his hand would not grope further and deeper.

"Pass, woman," the guard said, opening the door wide.

Before Iras could reach it the Queen had seized the basket. The old woman bowed herself out, closing the door tightly behind her.

And Cleopatra touched each fig as if it were a jewel, while her maids watched in wonder. Her fingers hovered over the fruit, dug deep inside the basket, and at last found the thing she was searching for.

She touched the cold thing, and a shudder ran through her. Then she lifted the tiny, poisonous serpent in both her hands and looked at it joyfully. Iras stifled a scream. Charmian clasped her hands, as frightened and yet as glad as was her Queen.

Cleopatra looked at both of them and said, "Good-by, dear friends." She raised her eyes and whispered, "Forgive me, Caesarion. Anthony—I will soon be with you." And she pressed the snake to her breast.

She sank back on her cushions, hardly aware that Charmian had taken the asp from her hands and had copied her actions, handing it then on to Iras to do the same. The Queen felt the poison working. It would only take a moment. Once these three had been young girls, beginning life together, playing together the childish game of "if Cleopatra were queen. . . ." Now they were dying together.

So Octavian found them. So perished one of the most incredible and glamorous women of all the ages.

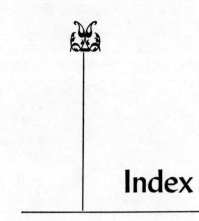

Index

About the Author

IRIS NOBLE grew up on a ranch in the Crow's Nest Pass between Canada's Alberta and British Columbia. Her parents were American and when she was eleven they moved to Oregon. After graduating from the University of Oregon, she moved to Los Angeles and got her first job as a secretary at station KFI-KECA. She left there to work for Fawcett Publications and later was publicity director for a theatre-restaurant. After her marriage she came to New York City where she did freelance writing. In recent years she has made her home in San Francisco and has been devoting herself to writing both in the field of biography and teen-age fiction.